WOODWORKING JOINTS

Woodworking Joints

Gordon Warr

Aidan Walker
Series Editor

ARGUS BOOKS

Argus Books Limited
Wolsey House
Wolsey Road
Hemel Hempstead
Hertfordshire HP2 4SS
England

First published by Argus Books 1989

ISBN 0 85242 957 6

Phototypesetting by Goodfellow & Egan Ltd., Cambridge
Printed and bound by LR Printing Services Ltd., Manor Royal, Crawley, West Sussex, RH10 2QN, England

CONTENTS

INTRODUCTION

Joints of one kind or another are probably as old as the use of wood itself. For joint really means where two or more components meet, and therefore wherever more than one piece of wood is used, then a means of securing them together has to be evolved. Pegs, usually of wood, are believed to be one of the earliest means of jointing wood, but the mortise and tenon also featured in the ancient products of the tree and the craftsman.

It is sometimes thought, in this modern technological age, that joints are rather old fashioned, that they are no longer needed and that all securing of components can be achieved with 'devices'. We now have extremely good and reliable glues, improved screw technology, bolts and fasteners, plates and brackets, and a whole assortment of ingenious hardware to make traditional jointing redundant. Not so, as traditional jointing methods which have stood the test of time are alive and well, and are especially important where quality is paramount. True, we do have available a vast and growing range of mechanical jointing devices but, for the most part, these are designed with man-made boards in mind, and are more applicable to mass production in factory woodworking than individual work either by the keen amateur or the small professional, producing for the most part one-off items.

Joints lie at the very heart of both woodworking skills and products, especially for furniture and allied work. While the ability to cut sound, well-fitting joints is important, I believe that every stage in a woodworking project is important, from the initial selection and preparation of the wood right through to the finishing. Each stage depends on the preceding one; however well the joints are cut they will not fit properly if the marking-out was itself poorly executed.

Times, though, do change, for as well as advancing technology relating to hardware, we now also have portable power tools and a wide assortment of attachments for them, small machines, and jigs of various types to aid us in our workshops, for even small workshops are rarely devoid of power assistance. All the signs are that the use of power will become more and more a feature of the workshop, and, while the serious woodworker will still use sound, well-tried jointing methods, the means of forming these joints are now more varied than ever.

Several books have been published in the past on the subject of woodwork joints. For the most part, these have tended to be encyclopaedias of joints, listing as many as possible with the emphasis on referring to almost every joint, however obscure, which has ever been devised. These books, therefore, have tended to be academic in their approach. This book takes a different approach. Rarely-used joints, and those which are of novelty interest only, do not appear. I have concentrated on what are still regarded as basic joints, along with their common variations, and make reference to the design of the joint relating to its proportions for strength, and its appearance where this is important.

Because of the increasing use of power tools and small machines, I show and discuss alternative ways of cutting joints. With the possible exception of 'biscuit jointing', all the joints are based on those which were evolved to be made by hand, using hand tools. Power, in whatever form it is used, allows us to make the same joints much more quickly than by hand, and especially so where an element of repetition is involved.

Power woodworking is not a substitute for hand skills, rather it augments whatever skills we have to make projects which are useful and functional, attractive and decorative, and modern or traditional. However, now we have a wider choice than ever before in how we fashion them.

CHAPTER 1

MARKING OUT

Although different joints are marked out in different ways, there are some general points to note which are common to all. Precise marking-out is a prerequisite for the cutting of good joints, and accurate preparation of the wood is essential for both the marking out and the forming of the joints. For the simplest of half laps, for example, if the thickness of the two pieces varies, then there will be surface misalignment on assembly. The wood must be prepared with the surfaces flat in both length and width, opposite surfaces parallel, and with the corners true right angles.

Uniform thicknesses are particularly important where power tools and machines are being used. This is because cutting often takes place from both surfaces, such as when the cheeks of a tenon are cut, where varying thicknesses of wood will result in differing sizes of tenons.

There are always exceptions to the above. Where a piece of wood is tapered, then it may be best to form the taper at the preparation stage. Where a member is tapered on both edges, however, tapering is best left until the joints have been marked and cut, or the marking out is unnecessarily complicated. Where a component has a curved outline, it has to be shaped at the preparation stage, normally with the aid of a template. Much of the marking out required can be transferred directly from the template, which should show the positions of the joints.

Rules, squares, bevels, and gauges are the essential tools for marking out, along with a marking knife and pencil. Gauges must have sharp points or cutters and the knife, too, must have a keen edge. Soft pencils are not suitable, and this includes the popular or everyday grade of HB. Soft pencils wear quickly, and such pencils make wide, clumsy lines which are far too wide for accurate work. I have found that the H grade pencil gives the best results, but it must have a point and not a rounded tip for precise work. Generally, lines along the grain are made with a gauge, while those across the grain are made with a try square used in conjunction with either a knife or a pencil. A cutting gauge is also used across the grain, normally only if the line is near the end of the wood which must be trimmed dead square beforehand.

My usual procedure is to make all lines across the grain initially in pencil. Those pencil lines which indicate a saw cut I then go over with the marking knife, as this emphasises the line by severing the surface fibres. However, lines made indiscriminately with the

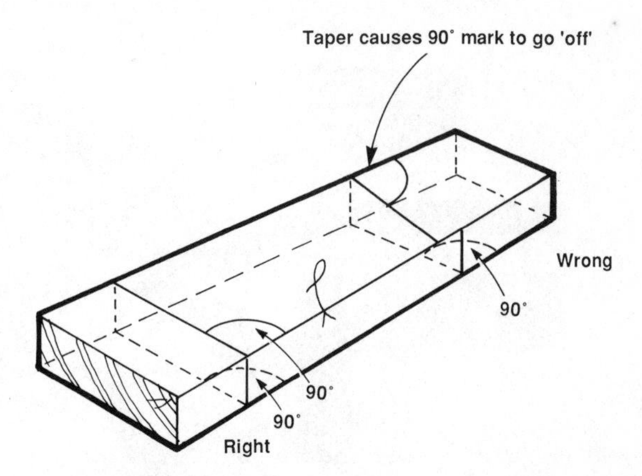

Fig. 1 *The importance of face marks when using a try square.*

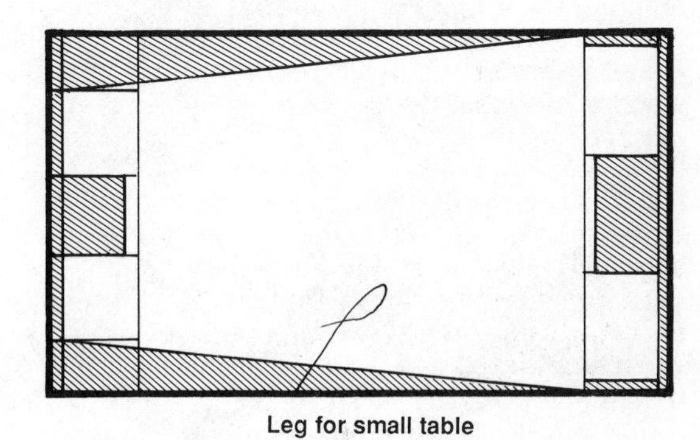

Fig. 2 *Where both edges are tapered, marking out is completed before shaping.*

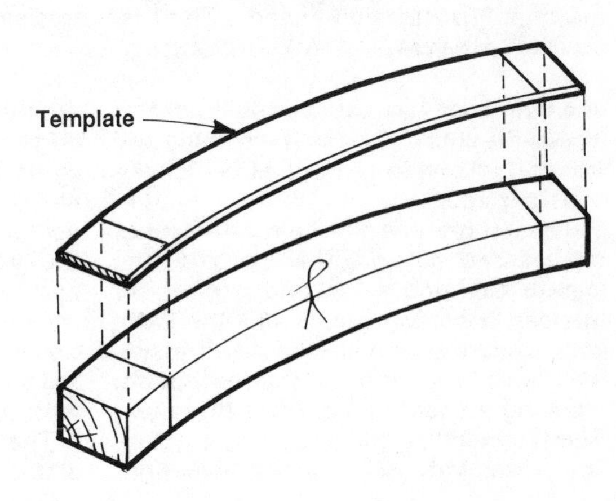

Fig. 3 *Using a template for marking out curved components.*

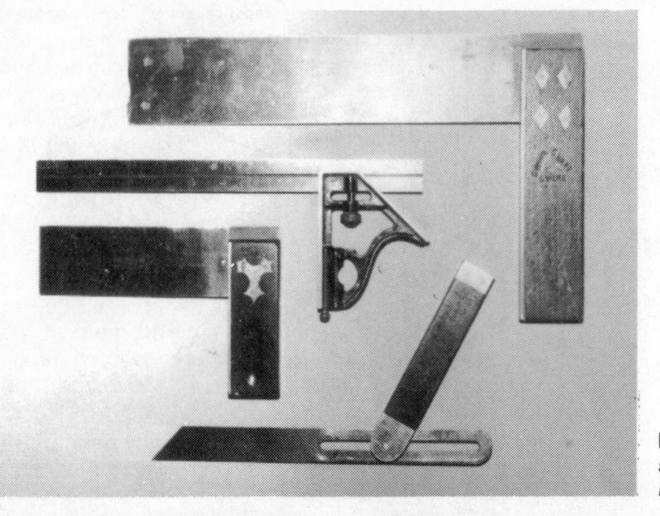

Fig. 4 *Assorted try squares and sliding bevel.*

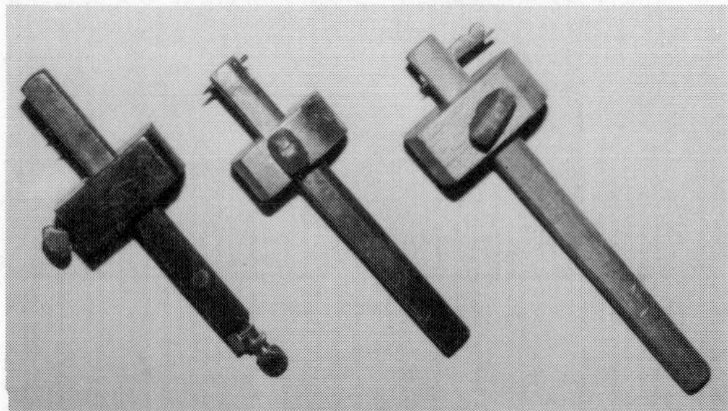

Fig. 5 *Mortise, marking, and cutting gauges.*

marking knife can cause problems later on, as the cuts go below the surface and can be difficult to remove at the 'cleaning up' stage.

The importance of face marks cannot be stressed enough. These provide the datum face and edge, and from these we can ascertain which are the front and back, top and bottom, and inside and outside. Almost without exception, marking out takes place from these two surfaces; that is, the square and gauge are used with their stocks held tight against either the face side, or face edge. The face marks and the wood must be arranged at the marking out stage so that a distinct pattern is established. Thus, for a simple framed door, the face sides should all face the front, and the face edges be to the inside. A common cause of error is failure to observe face marks, where the cut is made on the wrong surface, or the wrong part removed as waste.

The face marks are usually indicated at the preparation stage, as these are the first two surfaces to be planed. If for any reason they are not present, then they must be marked clearly and boldly. It often helps on more complicated projects, where a large number of components are involved, to make additional marks on the wood such as 'left hand', 'right hand', 'lower rail', 'drawer side', and so on.

As far as possible, similar components should have as much as possible of the marking out carried out while held together, usually gripped in the vice. This is not only quicker, but also far more accurate. Note that 'similar' components are not always 'identical'. For our framed door example, the two stiles are 'handed', and the lower rail is wider than the upper one. The stiles, therefore, must be held in the vice with the face marks opposing one another, but the face edges of both uppermost. Usually it is the 'length' positions which are marked when the parts are held together, then removed from the vice for individual squaring round and gauging.

If a tapered piece has a line squared round onto all four surfaces without regard to the face marks, then there is a strong possibility they will not meet. If the square is held against the datum surface as the line is squared from side to edge and edge to side, then they will meet accurately at each corner. With tapered work, it is best to make the line square to the face edge, and not the opposite edge.

Similar discrepancies can arise when a gauge is used. This must be held against the face side or face edge if consistency is to be maintained, or gauge lines which should meet at the ends will not meet. Even when a gauge is set to the centre of the wood, and when gauging from opposite surfaces should therefore result in such lines always being correct, gauging should still be from the datum surface. Should there be any slight discrepancy in the sizes of the different components which

Fig. 6 *(left).* **Fig. 7** *(below).*
All gauging is from the face side or face edge.

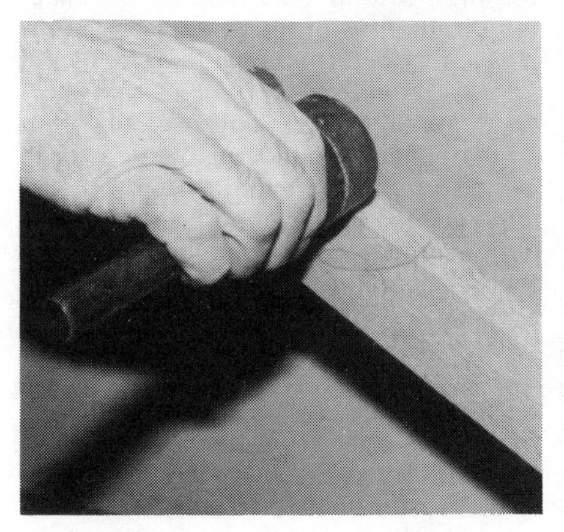

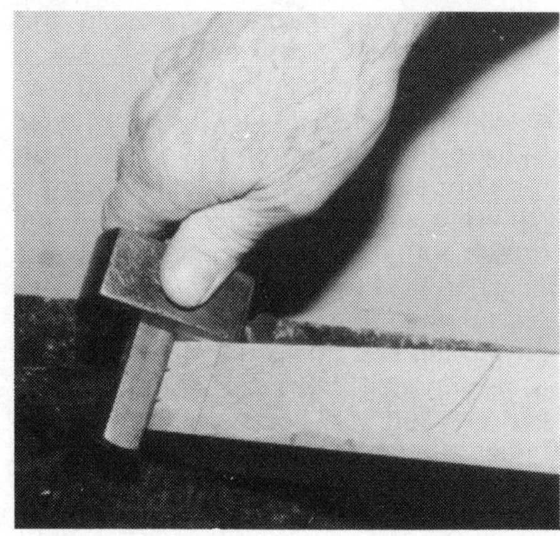

should be identical, then these variations will not be reflected in the gauging if carried out correctly.

It is sometimes advocated that, where a gauge line is not too clear, then a pencil should be run along the line in order to emphasise it. True, this does make the gauge line much more visible, but also far less accurate. What usually happens is that the pencil rubs along both sides of what is really a tiny groove made by the gauge. Thus two pencil lines are made, neither of which is central to the gauge line. This is bad practice. Far better to learn to use the gauge more effectively.

The usual order of working is to prepare the joints before forming other cuts, such as rebates, grooves, and moulded edges. It is far easier to both mark out and cut joints while the wood is still rectangular, but make such allowances as are required for subsequent cuts. Thus, for example, for a frame which is rebated on its inner edges, the joints would have to be made to allow for this, then the rebates formed once the joints are cut. This assumes the rebates are to be cut as through rebates before assembly, and not formed by router after assembly, although forming the rebates in this way can still affect the joints.

Generally, only those parts and surfaces which are actually going to be cut to form the joint are marked out. Thus, for a housing joint, there is little point in squaring the lines which indicate the trench onto all the surfaces of the wood. This can lead to error. Nevertheless, it's worth while to indicate exactly which is the waste, and this is usually done with a few pencil lines as shading. The experienced may scorn this, but for the uncertain, it's a worthwhile precaution. Even the experts will use some form of marking when the wood has to be cut in a fairly complex way.

It is common practice to leave a little extra on the length of the wood when it is being initially prepared, and to retain this extra length while the joints are being cut, even until after assembly. This is particularly true on pieces which are to be mortised near their ends, where the extra at the ends is known as either the 'horn', or the 'joggle'. It minimises any risk of the wood splitting, especially where the mortise is a through one and the tenons are to be wedged. Such excess length is removed after assembly, when the outer edges can be levelled and made smooth. However, the practice of leaving excess length on material does vary according to the nature of the work, the joints used, and how they are to be cut. For example, drawer components need to be trimmed to exact length before the joints are made, and this applies to all dovetails used for 'box' type constructions.

One of the particular advantages of using small machines is that, once set, repeat cuts can be made with great accuracy. Where joints are being formed by machine, there is often a case for first cutting the material to exact length, then using this end as a datum surface to determine the extent of the joint. In addition, for fairly straightforward joints, the marking out can often be simplified, and indeed in some cases even eliminated. Accuracy and consistency in this case depend on precisely dimensioned stock of absolute consistency, accurate setting of the machine, and careful checking of the 'sample' piece to ensure the cuts are exact in every way.

The essence of making good joints is to mark out accurately, and then remove the waste exactly up to the lines. By this I mean that there is no

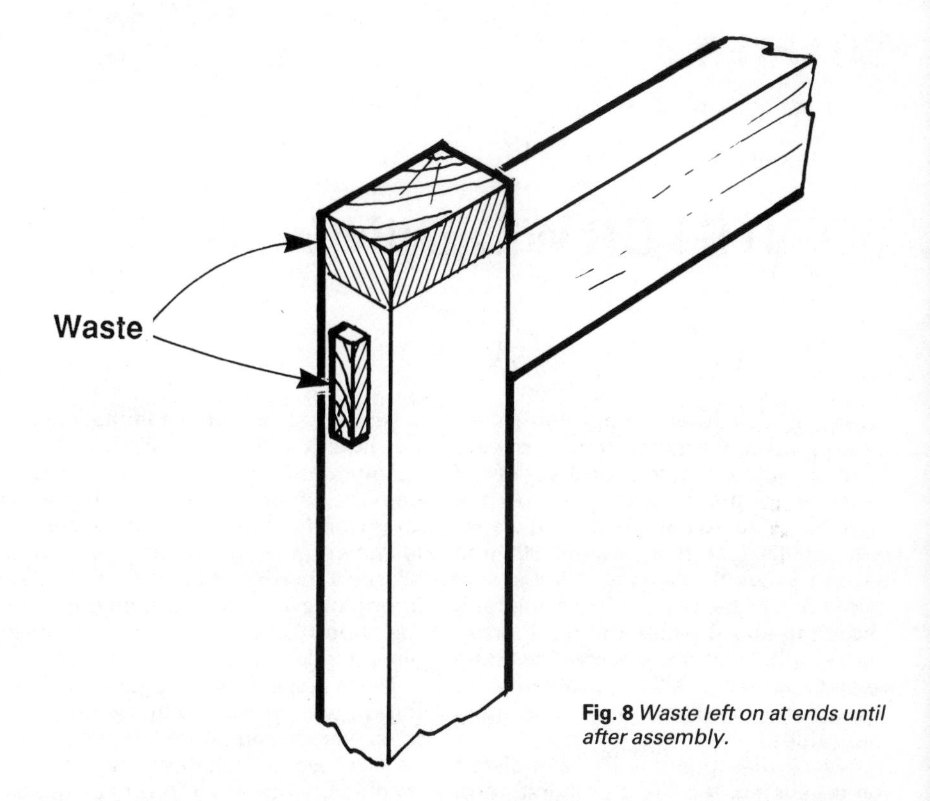

Fig. 8 *Waste left on at ends until after assembly.*

need to make allowances so as to produce a 'tight' joint, nor indeed to so mark out and cut that the joint will be slightly slack in order to aid assembly. True, it is wise to err away from the slack fit, and it also has to be kept in mind that often surfaces which are incorporated into the joint have to be 'cleaned up' before assembly, and this can affect their size and therefore the fit.

CHAPTER 2

JOINTS FOR WIDENING

Even though many imported hardwoods are converted from logs of very considerable diameter, for a variety of reasons by the time they are in the merchants' racks the boards and planks are usually less than around 300 mm (12 in.) in width. Although timber can occasionally be bought in double and more the above width, there are drawbacks with very wide stock, including seasoning and allied problems of distortion, handling, and machining difficulties.

A very wide board is likely to distort on seasoning, the most probable form of warping being in the form of cupping – failure to remain flat across the grain. Narrow boards can also cup on drying, but the extent of the distortion is proportionally far less. The likelihood of a board remaining flat depends upon the care taken during seasoning and on the position of the annual rings within the board.

Softwoods, especially those imported from Scandinavia and Russia, are usually converted from trees which are relatively small in diameter. Red deal, popularly referred to as pine but known as 'reds' or 'redwood' in the trade, is only rarely available over 250 mm (10 in.) in width, with the average being much less than this.

Because of the above limitations, we not infrequently find ourselves having to joint the boards together in order to gain the width required. This is particularly true for table tops. The technique is known as 'edge jointing' and, when properly carried out, the joint is as strong or even stronger than the rest of the wood, the joint line itself being almost indetectable.

There are, in fact, advantages in jointing up two, or more, narrow boards to make a wide component. Initial planing of the wood, whether by hand or machine, is usually more manageable, and handling, storing, and cost are more acceptable. The main gain of jointing, though, is that it gives the ability to produce a flat overall surface, with a better chance of this being retained.

Ideally, boards which are to be jointed together should be radially sawn, that is, have the annual rings running more or less at right angles to the face. Such boards are more likely to remain flat than are tangential sawn boards, where the annual rings run across the width when viewed from the end. Where tangential boards are being jointed, then it's good practice to alternate the way in which the heart side of the boards face. Thus, any tendency to

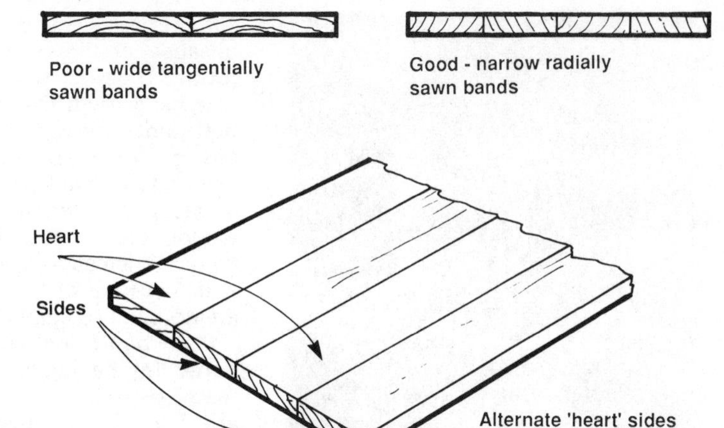

Fig. 9
Arrangement of grain when widening.

cupping is in part cancelled out. It should go without saying that wood for jointing must be well seasoned but even this is never a full guarantee against some subsequent distortion, however slight.

While there are a number of ways to joint the pieces together, all methods have one thing in common. The abutting edges must be dead true, so that when placed together they are a perfect fit. It is a mistake to rely on cramps to force poorly-fitting edges together, and likewise we should not expect glue to compensate for poor preparation.

It is possible for even two boards to abut in several ways, so at the outset the wood must be examined so as to arrive at the best way for them to be arranged with particular reference to the grain. In addition to the annual rings, the grain pattern on the face should be examined, as well as the direction of the grain. This means that, once jointed, any subsequent planing of the face would be with the grain on both or all component members. Once the best arrangement of the boards has been decided, then corresponding edges should be clearly indicated with identification marks.

A good planing machine properly adjusted should be capable of producing edges which are a perfect fit, although the accuracy does depend in part on the length of the planer tables in relation to the length of the wood. I have found that portable power planers, because of the fairly short length of the sole and especially in front of the cutters, do not give sufficient accuracy to the edges for jointing purposes.

When planed by hand, as long a plane as possible should be used, and ideally a trying plane is the one for the job. This must be both sharp and finely set. During planing, one edge should be tested against the other, and the closeness of the fit checked. Even a slight gap in the fit indicates there is a high area on one or both pieces, any tendency of one piece to seesaw on the other shows the same fault and the

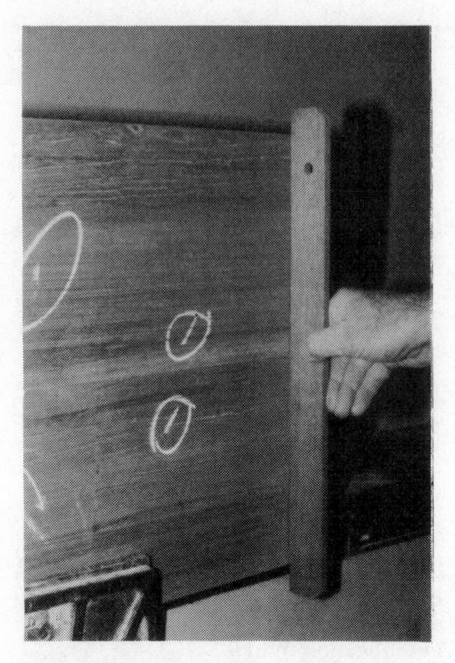

Fig. 10 *Checking face of boards with straight edge.*

need for further planing. Even one or two shavings can make a lot of difference, but the planing must always be carried out based on your testing and checking and not just randomly.

The edges must be exactly square, as well as being perfectly straight. Edges should be checked initially with a try square and, in addition, the overall flatness of the combined faces should be checked. If one is held in the vice with the other resting on it, then a straight edge held across the face of both reveals any inaccuracies. Even edges prepared by machine should be checked in this way.

BUTT JOINTS

Butt joints rely entirely on glue, and are sometimes called rubbed joints because of the way the pieces were rubbed together when hot animal glue was used. With the correct conditions, butt joints are very strong, but reliable glue of the proper consistency must be used and carefully applied. In addition, it must be remembered that some woods glue better than others. Oily woods, such as teak, are difficult to glue and, because of this, plain butt joints are not really suitable for these timbers.

Plain butt joints of any type are the better for having pressure applied to them, especially so where the pieces are fairly long. Ideally, sash cramps should be placed every 450 mm (18 in.) or thereabouts along the work. Alternate cramps should be placed on opposite sides of the assembly. If all the cramps are positioned just on the one side, then the wood may be forced into a bowed shape as pressure is applied. This is especially important with thin wood or the pieces can be forced right out of the cramps.

With the plain butt joint, it is essential to ensure that the faces of the boards remain in alignment. To help in this, G-cramps placed across each end of the assembly, with scrap wood between cramp and workpiece, will help considerably to ensure the surfaces remain level.

Any excess glue should be removed with a damp cloth before it sets. Not too damp, however, and beware of water or even dampness in the vicinity of the cramps, or staining can occur. This is particularly true of oak, which, because of its acidic nature, reacts with the steel in the presence of any water, and severe black stains can appear in a matter of hours. Water-based glues (the popular PVA) can themselves cause such ugly and well-nigh indelible marking.

What has been said above relating to

gluing, cramping, the danger of staining, and the need to remove excess glue while still wet, relates to assembling all joints. Failure to remove all traces of glue can cause problems at the finishing stage. Any glue remaining on the wood can have the effect of sealing the surface and this is likely to show as a lighter area even under the clearest of finishes.

LOOSE TONGUE

For most material of average thickness which is being jointed, the tongue is made from plywood, either 4 mm or 6 mm (3/16 in. or 1/4 in.) thick, cut to between 18 mm and 25 mm (3/4 in. and 1 in.) wide. With thin wood, the size of the tongue can be reduced and, on thick pieces, say over 44 mm (1.3/4 in.), then twin tongues can be employed. Where possible, the ply tongues should be cut across the grain as this gives more laminations running the short way, and thus maximum strength. It is essential for the grooves to be sufficiently deep to provide a little clearance for the tongue. The ply tongue does not have to be in one continuous length and there is no disadvantage in using several short pieces of tonguing.

While the tongue should not be a loose fit in the grooves, make sure that it isn't over tight. If too tight, the wood to the sides of the grooves will be forced outwards with this distortion creating a gap on the surface. The thinner the wood, the more likely this is to happen. Tongues can, of course, be made out of solid wood, but this does not have the cross-grain strength of ply. On the other hand, ply tongues are very conspicuous at the ends, whereas solid tongues are far less noticeable.

The traditional method of forming a groove is by the use of a plough plane, or combination plane. In the days when wooden moulding planes were in com-

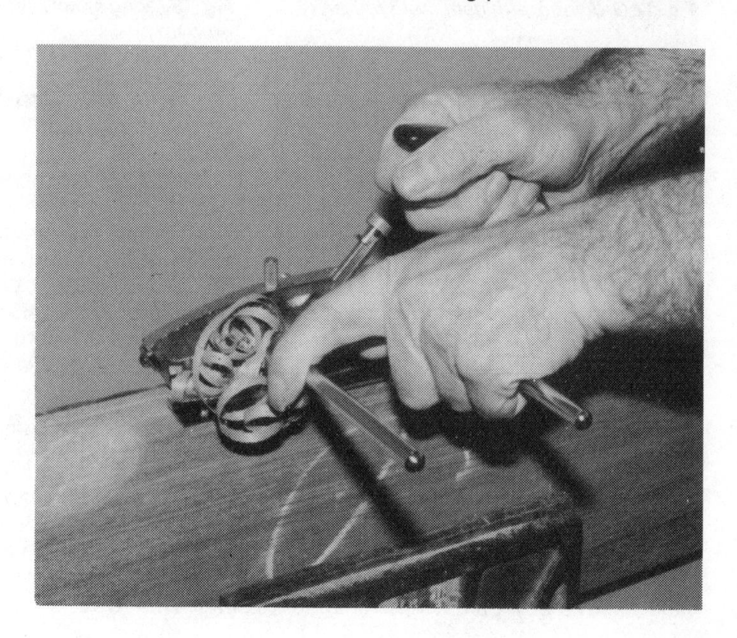

Fig. 11 *Forming groove with plough plane.*

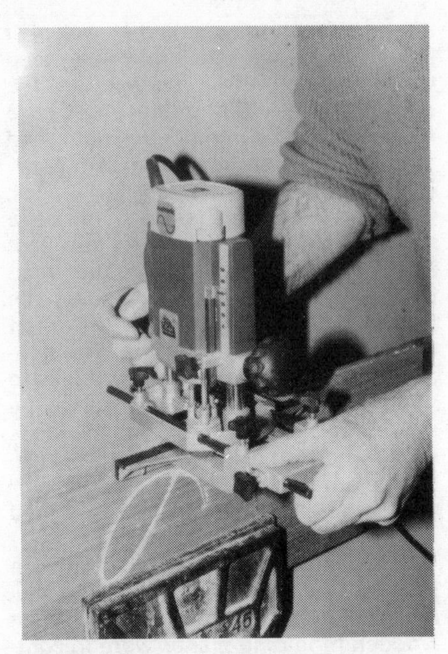

Fig. 12 *Grooving with hand held router.*

Fig. 13 *Using small router table when grooving.*

mon use, a variation of these tools was one specifically for grooving, and another to form a corresponding tongue 'in the solid'. These were known as matching planes, but they could of course be used independently. To cut a groove by hand, some kind of plane is essential.

The high-speed electric router is perhaps the most versatile of all the power tools, and it provides a very convenient way of forming grooves. One way of using the router is when held by hand, with a straight cutter fitted. Even with a powerful router, when the cutter is of fairly small diameter and the cut relatively deep in relation to this, then it is wise to form the groove by making two or more 'passes'. The fence of the tool must always be against the face side, then even if the grooves are not quite central, they will still properly align with one another.

The router and straight cutter can also be used when the router is in the fixed mode of working, when it is the wood which is moved past the cutter. The small router table from the Elu range is ideal for this, and remember to take note of the datum surfaces. Larger router tables, and many work centres, are also suitable.

The technology relating to routers and router cutters is advancing all the time, and cutters specifically for grooving are now available. These usually consist of an arbor onto which different cutters of varying sizes can be mounted, and they also incorporate a bearing. This type of cutter is only really suitable when the router is fixed in a table, and when advantage is taken of the bearing which is known as the 'pilot'. When the pilot is used, then the depth of groove is fixed. If a shallower groove is required, then the fence of the table must be used so as to limit the projection of the cutter. Because of the design of grooving cutters, the cut can only be made in one pass, but a reasonably powerful router is required because of the relatively large diameter of these cutters.

A bench circular saw can be used for grooving purposes, providing the projection of the blade above the table can be adjusted. Best results will be given by the use of a T.C.T. blade, and a number of passes will be required to give the width needed for the tongue.

Rebating attachments for power drills are really very small circular saws, and these are ideal for forming grooves. While both the width and the depth setting of these attachments are usually very limited, they are sufficiently adjustable to cope with most needs. Again, several passes will be needed, always with the fence held to the face side of the wood. Because of the small

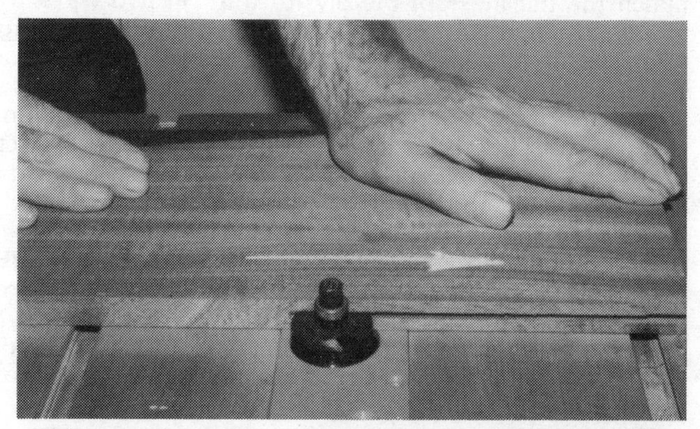

Fig. 14 *Special grooving cutter in use.*

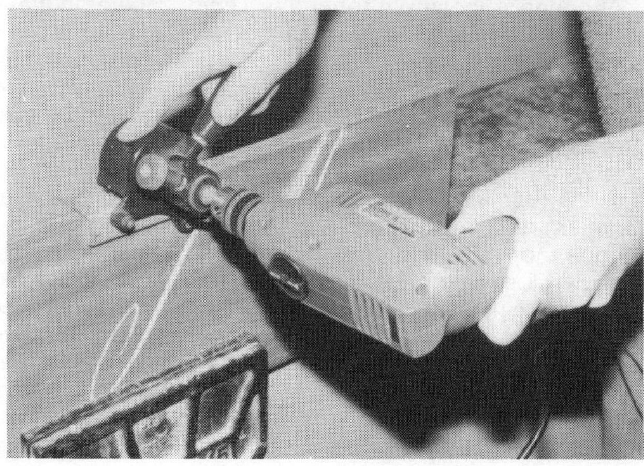

Fig. 15 *Power drill rebating attachment forming groove.*

diameter of the blade of these attachments, their cutting efficiency is best when used with a high-reving drill, but they operate over a wide speed range.

Rebating attachments can usually be fitted with cutters other than a small saw blade. These have multiple cutting edges and are normally known as milling cutters. Included among the range of cutters available are those specifically for grooving. They are, in effect, a wide type of circular saw, and are made to specific widths so as to produce a groove in one pass of that width. If the width of the cutter does not match the thickness of the ply for the tongue, then a second pass can be taken in order to widen the groove.

Milling cutters used with a power drill are not as efficient nor as clean cutting as are routers, but they can be useful for occasional use. It is possible to use milling cutters, and the small circular saw, in the stationary mode. Indeed, it is not difficult to make a table and adjustable fence for this purpose, with the drill being held on the underside of the table using either a 'drill guide', or 'drill clamp'. Router cutters cannot be used satisfactorily in a power drill.

Although a loose ply tongue is very strong, it does have the disadvantage of being visible as a part of the end grain. In many cases this will be of no consequence but, where the end grain will be on view on the completed project, then clearly through tongues are not suitable. The solution is to use 'stopped tongues', that is, the groove and the tongue stop a little short of the ends and therefore cannot be seen at all. The tongues are usually made to stop about 25 mm–40 mm (1 in.–1.½ in.) from the ends, after allowing for any waste to be removed after jointing.

It is almost impossible to form a stopped groove by hand with a plough or similar plane. All the other methods described are capable of forming stopped grooves, although a little hand work is likely to be required to complete the ends. Where any kind of saw or similar rotating cutter is used, then the end of the stopped cut will be curved according to the diameter of the tool used. This rounded end can be squared off by chisel. A router with a straight cutter will leave a small radius in the opposite plane to when saw-type cutters are used, and this is not likely to need any chiselling.

The tongue gives strength to the joint in two ways. There is some gain from the interlocking linking of the boards, but more important is the fact that the gluing area is increased considerably compared with a plain butt joint. The gluing area factor is an important consideration with most forms of joints.

SOLID TONGUE

This is where one board only is grooved, and the tongue formed directly on the edge of the second piece. One drawback is that it is not easy to achieve dead true surfaces to the rebates either side of the tongue, and another is the width sacrificed in order to produce the tongue.

By hand, the tongue can be formed by using a tonguing cutter in a combination plane, with a corresponding cutter used to form the groove. A router can also be used, again either handheld or used in a table, as can the rebating attachment already described. While it is possible to use a power plane provided it is equipped with a fence and depth stop, this is not as straightforward as it may seem. Because of the limited cutting depth of most power planes, several passes would have to be made, and this could lead to a loss of accuracy in the flatness of the final surface produced.

A planing machine can also be used to form rebates, but only if it is designed for this type of cut. Many planing machines will only allow for a depth-of-cut of around 3 mm (1/8 in.); this needs to be up to 13 mm (1/2 in.) for rebating, and with the infeed table extended sideways in order to support the work.

Solid tongues are not likely to be the first choice for edge jointing where the pieces are to be glued up to produce a single, wide component. However, edge jointing is not always glued, and this is particularly true where tongues and grooves are employed. Where a whole series of boards are produced in this way, and especially where they are relatively thin, say 16 mm (5/8 in.) or less, they are often known as 'match boarding'. Match boarding used to be used extensively for the backs of furniture, particularly what is often referred to as 'country-style' furniture for which it is still employed. Usually, the front edges of the boards are lightly chamfered to produce a 'V' effect on the front. This emphasises the board effect and also disguises any gaps which can open up between the boards should shrinkage occur. Remember that wood is more likely to shrink than swell, but 'movement' both ways is always possible and has to be allowed for where the width is considerable.

Boards prepared as above are known as tongued, grooved, and vee boarding, – T,G, & V, – and, for the backs of Welsh dressers and similar pieces of furniture, should be kept fairly narrow, say around 90 mm (3½ in.). Not only do narrow boards look better than wider ones, but also the amount of movement in narrow boards is proportionally less than wider ones. Match boarding is usually secured in place with pins or screws; glue is not used.

DOWELS

Although in this book there is a separate chapter on dowel joints and dowelling techniques, it is worthwhile in this section to look at the use of dowels to strengthen a butt joint.

The pieces to be jointed should be placed in the vice with the mating edges upwards, and the face sides facing outwards. The dowels need to be spaced at between 100 mm and 150 mm (4 in. and 6 in.) centres, and their positions squared across both pieces. If a dowelling jig is not being used, then a marking gauge is used to mark the exact position of the holes. The gauge is set to half the thickness of the wood and, by keeping the stock of the gauge to the face side, both pieces can be marked while held in the vice. When the holes are being bored freehand, then it helps if a small indentation is made with a pointed awl on the centre which provides a positive location for the bit.

Generally, the diameter of the dowels should be between one third and one half the thickness of the wood, and should penetrate 25 mm–30 mm (1 in.–1¼ in.) into each component. When boring freehand, care is needed to ensure the holes are square to the surface, and the extent of the boring should be governed by some means of depth control. Over-boring could mean an unequal distribution of the dowels across the joint and, if too shallow will prevent the tight fitting of the two edges.

Where the dowels are being prepared in the workshop, they must be cut a little shorter than the combined depth of the two holes. The ends need to be lightly pointed or chamfered, and have a groove formed along the length. The

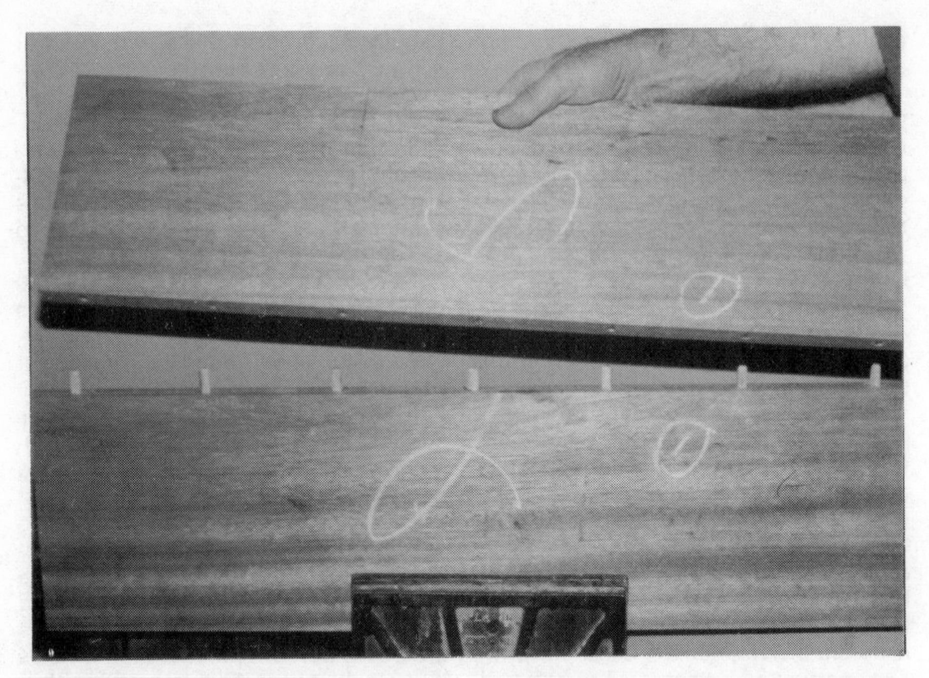

Fig. 16 *Assembling a dowelled butt joint.*

chamfer allows for easy location and penetration into the holes, and the groove allows excess glue to escape.

When assembling, the edges of both pieces are glued and glue is also introduced into the holes. This is best achieved with a slender piece of wood, and the dowels inserted into one of the pieces and tapped well down. The second piece is then slipped onto the dowels, and cramping follows the procedure as for a plain butt joint.

BISCUIT JOINTING

For this technique, a biscuit jointing tool is needed. There is no satisfactory alternative to this, and further information on biscuit jointing is given later in the book. When used for edge jointing, the method is a cross between dowelling and tonguing, and there is a choice of three sizes of biscuit to adopt. The spacing of the biscuits should be as given before for dowels, and for this particular use of biscuits the largest size is preferred. The thickness of all three sizes is the same.

CHAPTER 3

HALF LAPS

Like all joints used in woodworking, half laps have a number of basic forms and several variations. In addition, joints are often used in combination, for example the dovetailed halving, and the mitred corner halving, halvings being an alternative name for half laps. However, the basic principles of marking out and cutting of many types of joint apply in half laps.

The simplest form of half lap is the corner joint. Both parts of this joint are identical except that they are cut on opposite sides of the wood. This is more important than might at first appear although I have already referred to the importance of the face marks. The tee halving incorporates a slot known as a trench, while a cross halving embraces trenches on both components. The dovetailed halving is similar to the tee halving, this form of the joint being of particular benefit where there is a direct pull on the joint.

MARKING OUT

The location of the joint is initially marked out with try square and pencil, marking all similar pieces while held together. These lines are squared round the wood, although with experience time can sometimes be saved by squaring only on those surfaces where cutting will take place. An ordinary marking gauge is used to complete the marking out. The gauge is set to exactly half the thickness of the wood and, while a rule can be used for this, checking the setting on the wood is quick and simple. The gauge is held against one

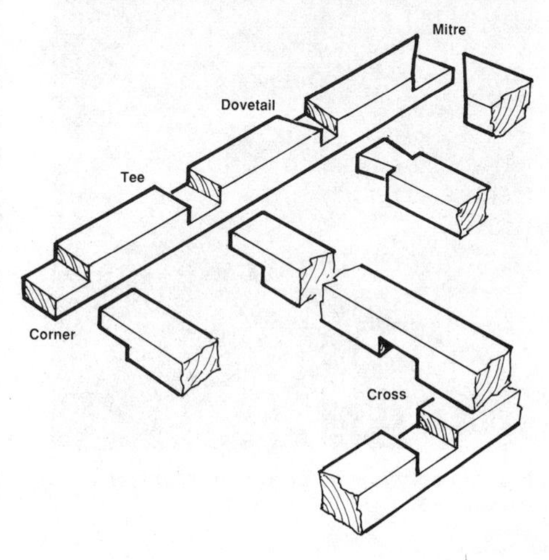

Fig. 17 *Basic forms of halving joints.*

side, and a small mark made with it on the edge; this is then repeated with the gauge held against the opposite side when the two marks should coincide. If not, the gauge is adjusted until the marks made are at exactly the same point, which is the centre. Remember the golden rule, which is that the gauging is carried out with the stock held tight to the face side. It is always worth while to indicate by marking which half of the joint is to be cut away as waste.

CUTTING BY HAND

If you are a relative beginner, go over those pencil lines where actual sawing is to take place with a marking knife. This severs the surface fibres, and gives a crispness to this part of the cutting. As an additional aid to accurate sawing, a 'vee cut' can be made within the waste. This is carried out by chisel. Making vee cuts is a particularly useful dodge for the fairly inexperienced to gain proficiency, although it is a stage the experts are likely to omit, except possibly where the wood is quite wide. Vee cuts, or indeed the marking knife, would only be employed where the joint is being formed by hand methods.

Fig. 18 *Forming vee groove with chisel.*

When cutting by hand, the waste at the corner halving is cut entirely by saw, and is a typical use of the tenon saw. It does not matter whether sawing down the grain or across the grain takes place first, providing the lines are adhered to. Sawing is always on the waste side of the line, and exactly up to it. Cutting across the grain is rather easier than sawing down the grain, and this part is known as the 'shoulder'. The wood is held on a sawing board for this rather than the vice, although it helps to grip the sawing board in the vice.

When sawing down the grain, the wood is placed fairly low in the vice, and cutting started on the furthest corner. By lowering the handle of the saw, the cut being made is always in view and, with the front end of the saw remaining just in the corner initially cut, sawing is continued until the shoulder line is reached. The wood will probably need to be tilted to achieve this, then it is reversed to complete the cut. This part of the joint is known as the 'cheek'. Accurate cutting down the grain demands a saw in good condition, otherwise drifting to one side is likely to occur, when following the line becomes very difficult.

If the sawing has become slightly inaccurate and a little additional trimming is required, this should be done with a sharp chisel. Remember, a small amount removed can make a lot of difference, and therefore frequent

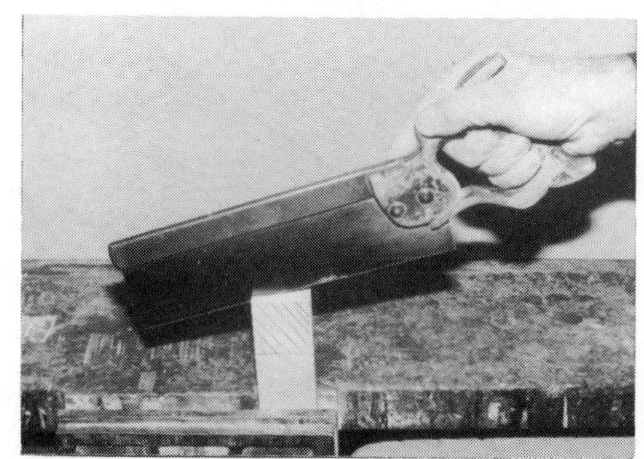

Fig. 19 *The start of sawing down the grain.*

Fig. 20 *Wood ready to be reversed.*

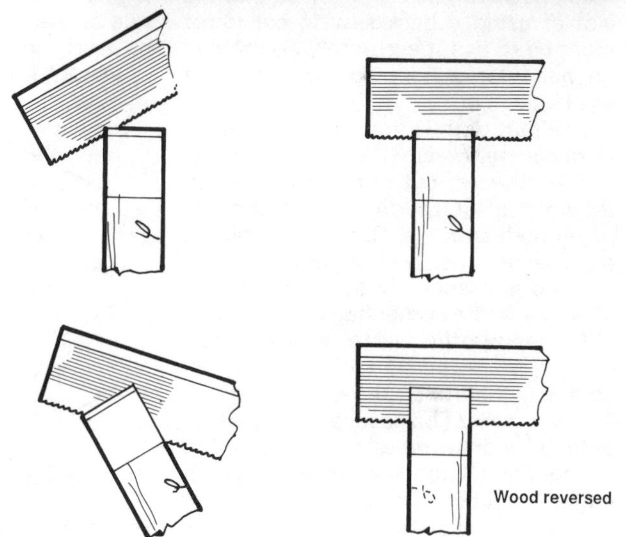

Fig. 21 *Stages in sawing the cheek.*

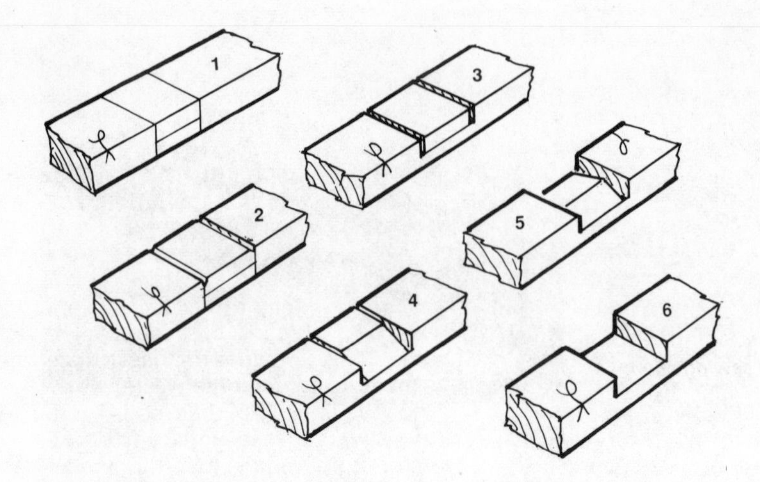

Fig. 22 *Stages in forming a trench.*

checking is required. A file, or glass-paper, should never be used to 'ease' this or any other joint, or level off inaccurate sawing. Files and glasspaper will make a surface smooth but rarely flat, especially where the area is small. Some rounding over invariably results from the use of abrading methods. It must, however, be emphasised that the aim of using a back saw to cut joints must be to use it accurately so there is no need for subsequent trimming of any kind.

One part of the joint for a tee-halving is, of course, exactly the same as for the corner halving, but forming the trench requires a quite different technique using both saw and chisel. The ends of the trench must be cut first, and this method is essentially the same as the shoulder of the corner halving.

To remove the waste, a bevel edge chisel is preferred, and the largest available to fit the trench should be selected. The wood must be securely held, either in the vice or cramped to the top of the bench. Chiselling takes place from both edges, although the aim should be to remove the waste a small amount at a time. The chisel is held flat side to the wood, and in the early stages is used with a mallet. Chiselling should always be from the edge towards the centre, so that the gauge line always remains in view and, therefore, the wood has to be reversed as the chiselling proceeds. For the final stages, the mallet is dispensed with and hand paring employed. A steel rule or the edge of a try square should be used across the bottom of the trench to ensure it is flat. If this joint is made

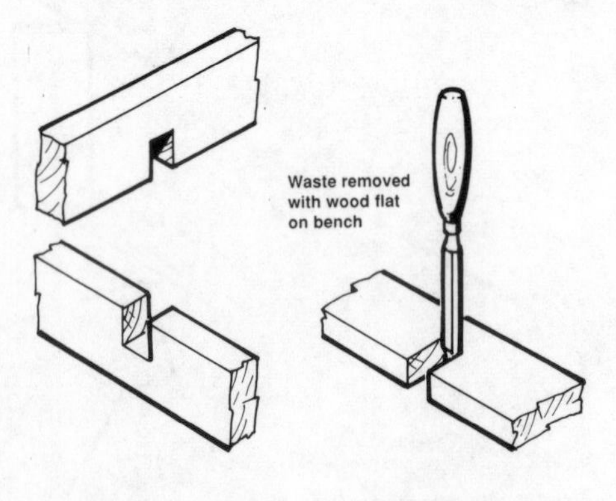

Fig. 23 *Half laps formed on edge of wood.*

too tight, then the wood can distort, especially if relatively thin.

Cross halvings are often used when the wood is on edge rather than flatways and, because of this, the chiselling of the trenches is a little different from that just described. After sawing the edges of the trench, the waste is best removed by chiselling downwards with the wood flat on a chiselling board. A mallet can be used in the early stages to remove the bulk of the waste, then the chiselling takes place from each side until the gauge lines are reached, with the chisel being held vertically. Testing after chiselling is always worth while to check for flatness.

CUTTING ON A SAW BENCH

The above forms of this joint can be cut entirely on a saw bench, providing the depth-of-cut can be adjusted and a cross cut fence is available. The projection of the blade above the table needs to be set to the gauge line, that is, half the thickness of the wood, and the cross cut (or mitre) fence must be checked for 90 degrees. This should be carried out by taking a trial cut and testing with a try square. A visual check of the protractor scale is insufficient, scales of any type being best regarded as only approximate guides.

When removing the waste from a tee halving, the first cut is best taken at the shoulder line. A series of passes are then made to remove the waste, working towards the end of the wood. There are two advantages in working from the shoulder to the end – first, the end of the wood is supported until the last cut is made and second, a 'full' cut is made at the shoulder. If cutting takes place towards the shoulder, then the last pass in order to reach the line might be of only part the width of the blade. Such

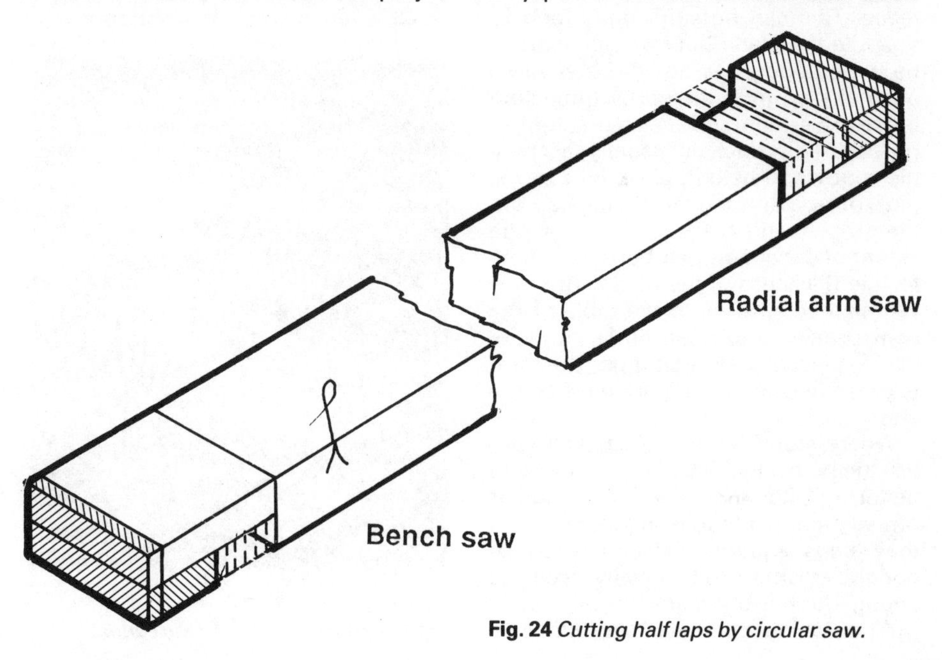

Fig. 24 *Cutting half laps by circular saw.*

cuts have a tendency to run slightly out of square, because the resistance offered to the blade is greater on one side than the other. I admit both the above are small points, but they are worth noting. Cutting must only take place on the forward movement of the wood, and the wood returned to the front of the table by allowing the blade to pass through the kerf just made. It is highly dangerous to attempt to make an actual cut on the backwards movement of the wood. The wood can be snatched by the blade and thrown at the operator.

It is possible to take advantage of a length 'stop' when forming tee halvings, and in fact similar other joints where the cutting takes place on the circular saw. The stop can be arranged in a number of ways. Most cross cut fences allow for a piece of wood to be secured so as to extend the face of the fence. This can be sufficiently long to straddle the blade but must, of course, be wide enough as not to be severed once passed over the partly projecting blade. This then allows for the stop to be secured, which is usually a small piece of wood held in place by screws, pins, or by cramping. The distance from the stop to the blade must equal the extent of the cut, remembering to allow for the thickness of the blade. The stop can also be secured to the table of the saw, providing this can be firmly held, which is usually by G-cramps. The third alternative is to use the rip fence as the stop.

Where stops are being used to control the point at which the shoulder is to be formed, it is essential that all similar pieces are first cut to exact length, with their ends square. 'Existing' ends of bought stock are not usually accurate enough for this purpose.

When using a circular saw blade in any kind of powered saw, it is desirable to use one with T.C.T. teeth. Apart from the long life from one sharpening which these blades give, they are more accurate than a standard plate blade and they also give a far smoother finish. A blade with fine cross cut teeth is to be preferred.

CUTTING ON A RADIAL ARM SAW

The basic procedure for cutting corner, tee, and cross halvings on a radial arm saw is the same as on a saw bench. This includes starting to remove the waste by sawing at the limits of the joint, and the use of stops. One difference between using these two types of saw relates to the presence of debris, usually in the form of sawdust, on the saw table. Sawdust trapped between the workpiece and the table when using a bench saw will result in the cut being made slightly less deep than it should be. On a radial arm saw, the opposite is

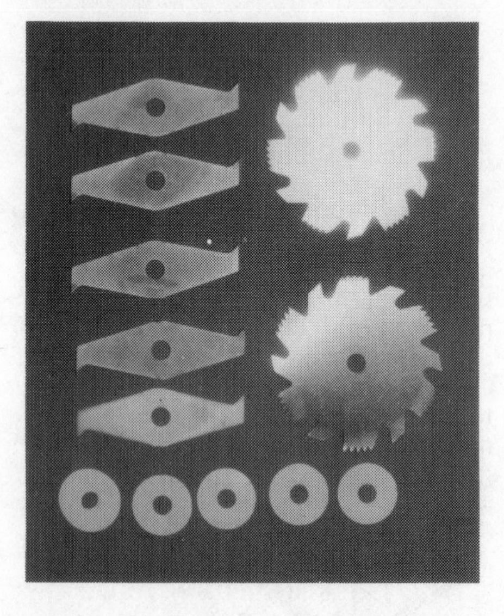

Fig. 25 *Popular quality of dado cutter.*

Fig. 26 *Premium quality dado cutter.*

Fig. 27 *The dado cutter in use.*

true. Sawdust beneath the workpiece raises it further into the blade, with the result that the sawing takes place beyond the gauge line. Cleanliness leads to accuracy, and the tables of all machines must be kept free of debris at all times.

Because a radial arm saw is designed to accept a wide range of supplementary equipment, this machine lends itself particularly to cutting half lap and similar joints when fitted with a dado cutter in place of the normal blade. In principle, a dado cutter is a form of circular saw blade which is adjustable in width, its main function being for forming housings, or trenches. Two popular types are available, one made from tool steel with fairly fine teeth, the other with large teeth tipped in either stellite or T.C.T. The design in both cases is such that some of the teeth are angled so as to sever the fibres, with the remainder sharpened square across so as to leave the bottom of the cut quite flat. Adjustment of the width of the cutter and therefore the cut can be made from around 10 mm to 22 mm (⅜ in. to ⅞ in.). This means that while the waste to a half lap joint cannot be made in a single pass, cutting is several times faster than using a circular saw blade.

Fig. 28 *Removing waste on router table. Guarding removed for clarity. Equipment in condition shown does not comply with Woodworking Machines Regulations 1974.*

CUTTING BY ROUTER

The most satisfactory way of forming half laps by router is to use this tool when secured to a table. A cutter of average size, say around 13 mm (½ in.) diameter, gives the best results; it must have 'bottom out' which in this case means that a cut is made across the top of the cutter. A cross cut fence is essential. Where a fine adjustment screw can be fitted to the router, this is advantageous in setting the height of the cutter and therefore the depth of the cut. A stop is essential, and for cutting the joints at the end of the wood the fence of the table can be used. Because the rotation of the cutter is in the vertical plane, as distinct from a circular saw blade which rotates in the horizontal plane, there is a tendency for the cutter to move the wood sideways. This is a further reason why a stop must be employed. Where a tee halving is being formed, the trench requires special care because of the possibility of sideways movement. A false fence of wood can be secured to the cross cut fence, and a stop secured at each end of this so that the distance apart equals the length of the wood plus the width of the trench. Thus, the wood when held against the fence is constrained to move laterally by the width of trench required, and unintentional drift beyond this avoided.

An alternative to this is to use abrasive paper to create friction between the workpiece and the fence. This is best secured to a piece of wood and, in turn, fixed to the fence. This method should be restricted to where the wood and therefore the joints are fairly small; the lighter the cut the lesser are the forces involved. Abrasive paper on the mitre fence is a useful dodge to adopt even for normal use of the fence when cross cutting, and especially where a lot of cutting at angles other than 90 degrees is made. For mitre cuts of any angle made on a bench saw, there can be a tendency for slight sideways drift, and the friction created by the abrasive sheet eliminates this.

USING WORKCENTRES

Workcentres are designed to allow a number of portable power tools to be used in the static mode, and thus convert them into small machines. The most popular power tools to be accommodated in workcentres are circular saws, routers, and jigsaws, some being designed to hold planers, sanders, and drill stands. The usual method of incorporating a portable power saw into a workcentre is for it to be fixed beneath the table so that it becomes a small sawbench. Thus, the combination so created can be used for the cuts already described for a standard sawbench. However, it must not be assumed that all power saws normally used hand held are suitable for use in this way. Only better-quality saws can be used for precision work. Lower-priced ones frequently develop some lateral play in the arbor, referred to as 'float', and such a saw is unsuitable where considerable accuracy is needed. In addition, a more suitable blade than that normally supplied with the saw, whatever the quality of the tool, will be needed for joint cutting. Most portable circular saws intended for the usual hand held method of working are at their best when ripping, and work where accuracy is not too important.

Certain workcentres allow for a circular saw to be used in an additional way to that which is similar to a sawbench. This is where the saw is mounted normal way up in a carriage which in turn slides across the table in rails. The work to be sawn is positioned beneath the blade and this remains stationary while the saw is moved along the rails to make the required cut. This set-up is also suitable for cutting certain joints, including halvings, the method of working being similar to using a radial arm saw.

When they have a router fixed to them, workcentres operate in the same way as a table designed more specifically for router work. However, those workcentres which allow for a circular saw to be used when sliding across the table with the wood stationary will also allow for a router to be mounted and used in exactly the same way. This gives a further option for removing the waste but, by whatever means a router is used, lateral restraint of the wood is essential.

Other Variations of Lap Joints

All lap joints are variations of the three basic types so far discussed, and for the most part cutting them follows the hand or alternative methods described. Let us take a look at some of the common variations.

Dovetail Halving The tongued component has its edges marked to a slope of approximately 1:7, and to make sawing easier the wide part of the joint is made a little narrower than the width of the wood. The slope can be marked with a sliding bevel, or a simple template can be made. This part of the joint is cut first, and is started by cutting away the waste from the rear of the dovetail. The sloping edges are always best cut by hand, and the saw can be angled by a very slight amount so that just the smallest of bevels is created on these surfaces. Only a hint of an angle is required.

Joints incorporating the dovetail are the only ones where one part of the

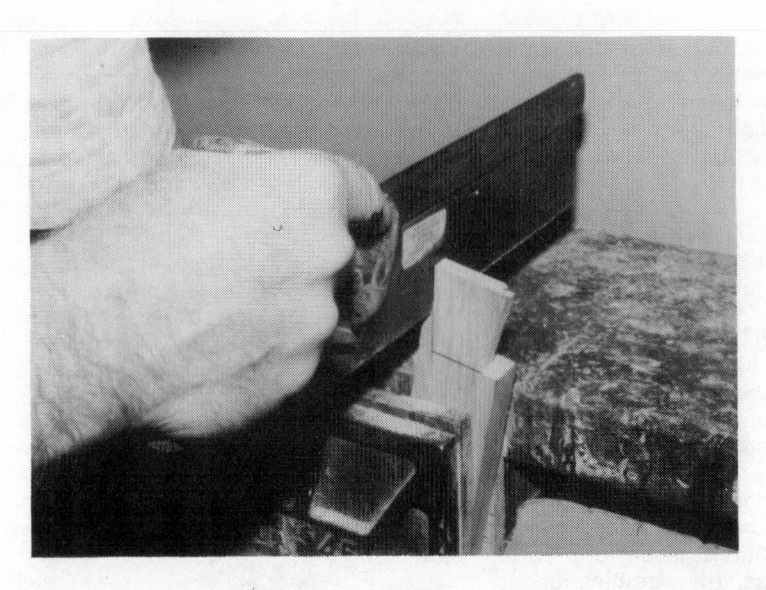

Fig. 29 *Cutting the dovetail halving.*

joint is marked by pencilling directly around the other. However, before this is done, the position of the cross rail should be squared across as for a tee halving. The 'tail' part of the joint just cut is placed directly over where it is to be fitted, and marked around with a sharp, well-pointed pencil. It is important to make identification marks on each corresponding part of all such joints so that they will be assembled in the positions they were in when marked and cut.

When cut by hand, this is essentially the same as if the limits of the trench were parallel. When cut by any of the other methods suggested, the ends of the trench are still cut by hand. The waste is then removed to correspond to the narrower part of the dovetail slope, and finally the remainder of the waste is removed by chisel.

The secret of successful dovetailing lies in cutting the second half of the joint, particularly where the outer limits of the waste are sawn. The sawing must be on the waste side of the pencil lines made to indicate the slope, but so that the line is just, and only just, left on. It is a mistake to saw well away from the line and then rely on a 'fitting stage' with the chisel in order to gain the fit needed. Any easing of any joint which is a little too tight must be done with great care; it only takes the removal of a small amount of wood to make a potentially good-fitting joint into a poor one.

Angled Halvings Although most joints meet at right angles, this is not always the case and joints at angles other than 90 degrees can be made. A sliding bevel is used for the marking out of joints of this type, the cutting being basically the same as for normal halvings. Extra care is required when marking out these joints to ensure the slope is in the right direction, and correct 'matching' is essential as each part of these joints is not identical with its opposite component, as is the case with right angled joints.

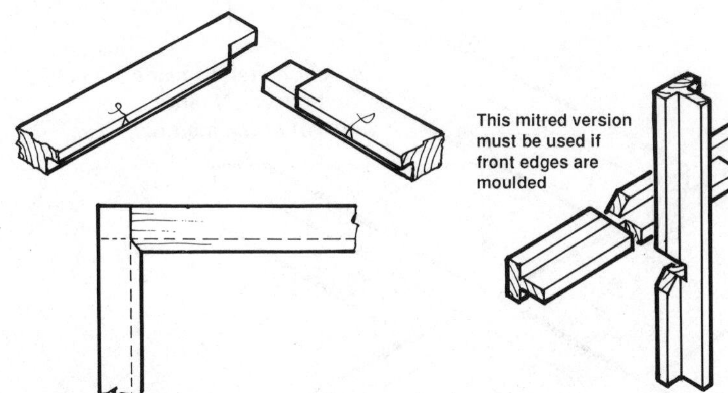

Fig. 30 *Corner halving with rebated material.*

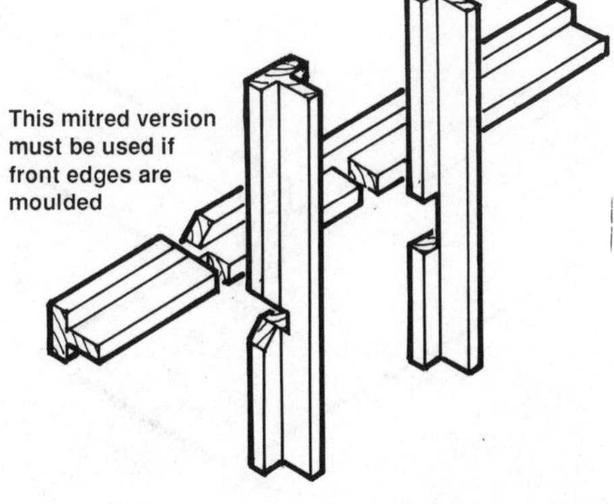

Fig. 31 *Halvings joints for glazing bars.*

Halvings on Moulded Members Sometimes we are faced with forming half laps in wood which has to be rebated or have the edges moulded. In these cases, the moulded or rebated part of the joint is mitred. The usual method of forming the mitre is with the aid of a mitre template and fairly wide chisel.

Cross halvings which incorporate mitres are amongst the options available for the intersection of glazing bars. Here, it is usual to make the depth of the trenches equal to the rebate, even if this is not actually in the centre of the wood.

Lap Joints other than Half Laps Because half the wood is cut away in a normal halving, it follows that there is a fairly considerable loss of strength which can vary in its significance according to the nature of the job. Where strength is important, and where it can be conveniently arranged, lap joints can be made where less than half the wood is cut away. These variations retain the positional location benefit of the joint, but with minimal loss of strength. Only about a quarter of the thickness of the wood is removed for these joints.

Fig. 32 *Under framing to small table – lap joints cut less than half way.*

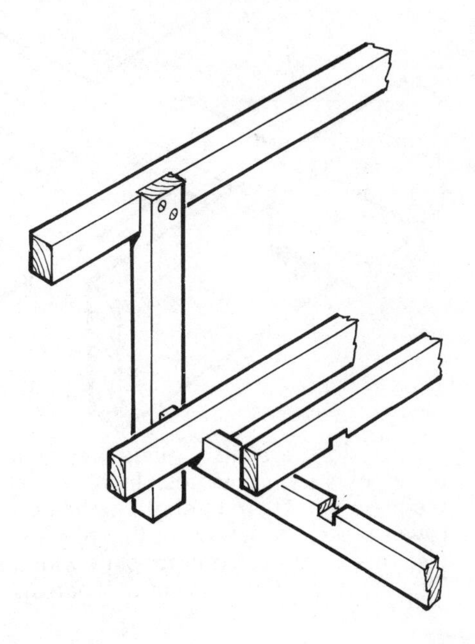

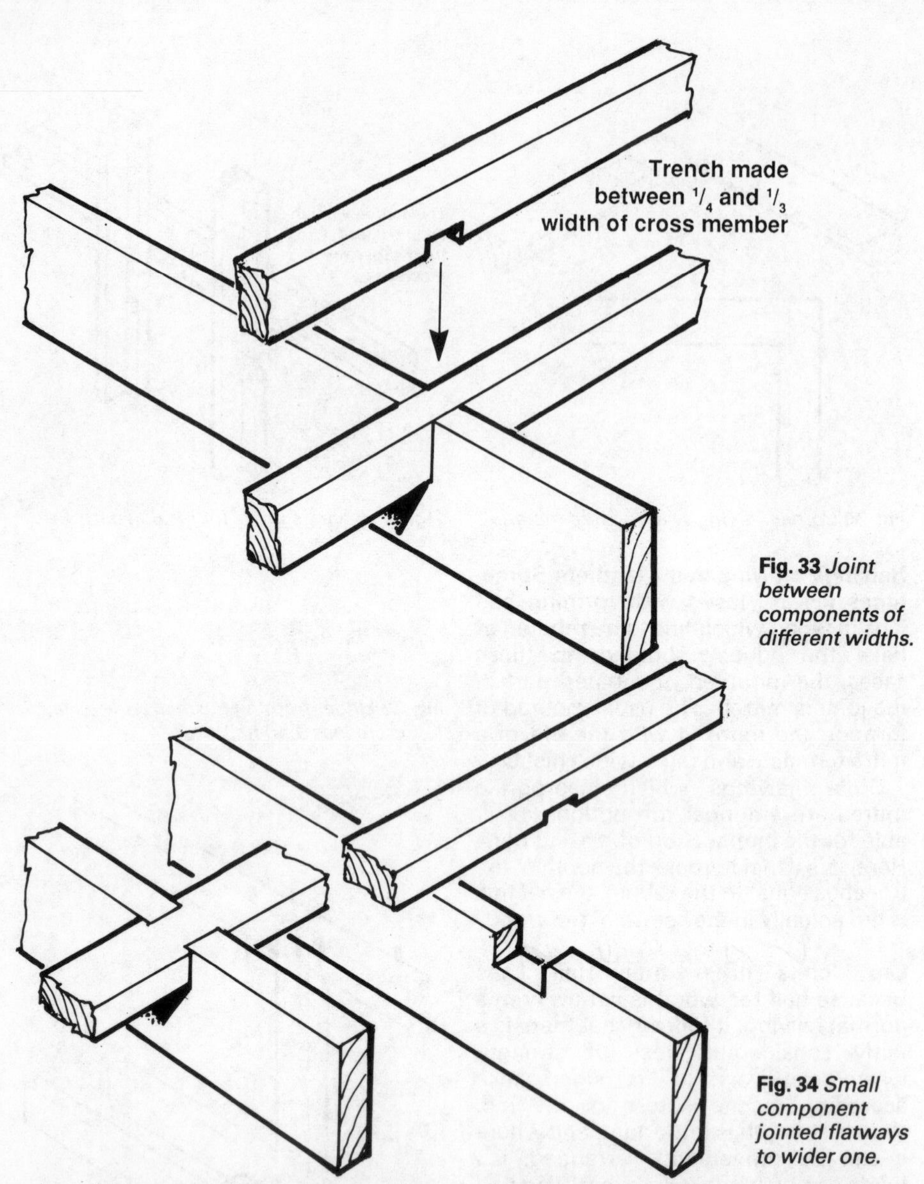

Fig. 33 *Joint between components of different widths.*

Fig. 34 *Small component jointed flatways to wider one.*

Lap joints are also made between wood of varying widths. In order to maintain maximum strength in the narrower piece, the trench in this piece is also made around a quarter of its width. The same applies to where a narrow member is being jointed flatways to a wider component. Where a wide piece is jointed to the edge of a member, then the wide piece as well as being trenched on its lower surface can have trenches formed in its edges.

CHAPTER 4

BRIDLE JOINTS

BASIC BRIDLE JOINTS

The simplest form of bridle is where the sizes of both components are the same. Although the bridle joint would be quite satisfactory in such a situation, in practice, however, the mortise and tenon would normally be considered to be more suitable. Indeed, the bridle is in many ways similar to the mortise and tenon, but with the opposite parts of each member removed as waste.

Whereas the mortise and tenon joint is used where the thickness of the components is the same, or where the thinner piece is being jointed to a thicker one, the bridle is more often chosen

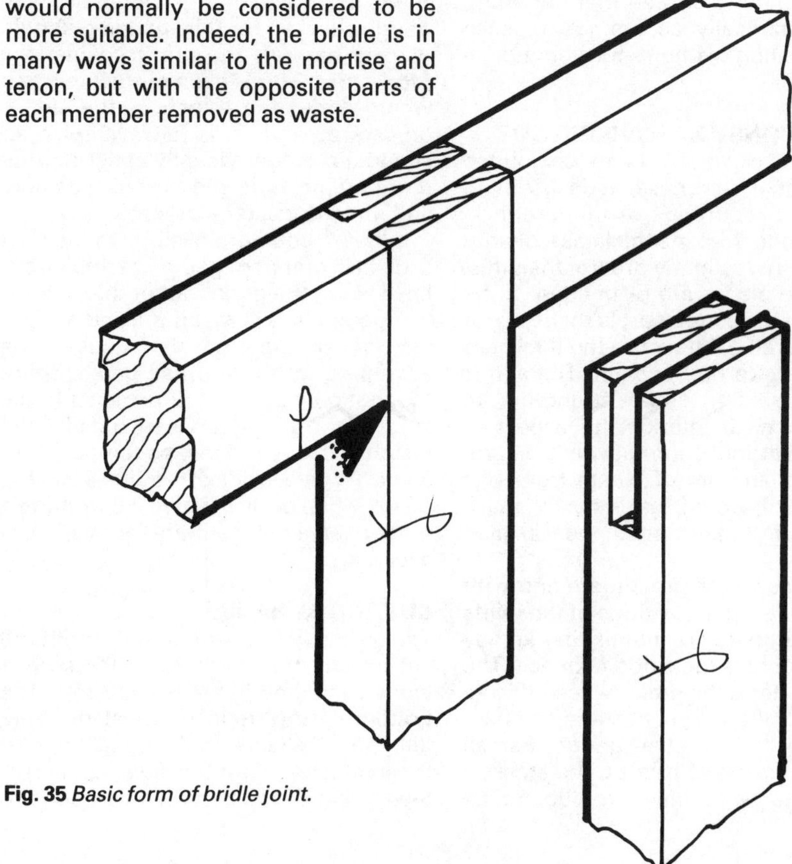

Fig. 35 *Basic form of bridle joint.*

where the thicker member is being jointed into a thinner one. Typical uses of these basic bridles are for the underframes of small tables, and plinths of cabinets.

Another common form of basic bridle is as a corner joint. This well illustrates the similarity to the mortise and tenon, in fact this particular bridle could quite properly be called an open mortise and tenon, – 'open' because the 'mortise' is open at one end. The corner bridle can also be made as a mitred version, as not only does this give a neat appearance to the face, but it also means that if the front inner corner is chamfered, moulded, or similarly treated then the mitre will automatically accommodate such edge profiling without further adapatation.

PROPORTIONS AND MARKING OUT

Where the components to be jointed are of equal thickness, it is usual to make the proportions of the interlocking parts one third the thickness, or with the centre part slightly greater than this. Where the pieces are of unequal thickness, then the centre part is made about a half or even a little more the thickness of the piece to be trenched. The aim is always to gain maximum strength from the mechanical interlocking aspect of the joint, without cutting away a disproportionate amount of waste from one piece which would, as a result, make this part of the joint much weaker than the other.

For joints which are square and with parallel sides, the positions of the joints on the members are initially marked by squaring across the wood in pencil. The two lines along the grain which indicate the extent of the trenches and slots are marked with a mortise gauge. For all but the simplest of bridles, the stock of the gauge will have to be re-set between gauging corresponding parts. The distance between the pins, though, remains the same. What is important in marking this, and indeed all other joints, is that similar components are gauged at the one setting before any adjustment to the gauge takes place for marking other members.

Gauging endgrain always presents some difficulty in order to indicate lines which are clear and true. One way of overcoming this difficulty is to hold the wood in the vice with the end to be gauged uppermost. Correctly carried out, the lines should meet exactly at the corners. Even where the joint is being made centrally in the wood and the gauge checked for this, gauging should always be with the stock against the face marks. This is even more important where either the trench or the slot is off-centre, and it is always wise to spend a moment visually checking that the gauging is in the correct position, and that the waste is indicated.

It is of course possible to use an ordinary marking gauge to make the lines along the grain, rather than a mortise gauge. It will mean making a number of settings of the gauge, the advantage of the mortise gauge being that not only are the adjustments to the stock of the gauge reduced, but also the distance between the pins remains constant. Angled bridles require a sliding bevel, while bridles which incorporate a mitre need a mitre square for maximum accuracy.

CUTTING BY HAND

The trenches to one half of the joint are cut exactly the same as for cross halvings described in the last chapter. The bottom of the trenches must be quite flat and cut exactly to the gauge lines. If the joint is too tight because of inaccurate cutting of the trenched component,

Fig. 36 *(top). Sawing waste from bridle joint.*

Fig. 37 *(right). Trimming end with mortise chisel.*

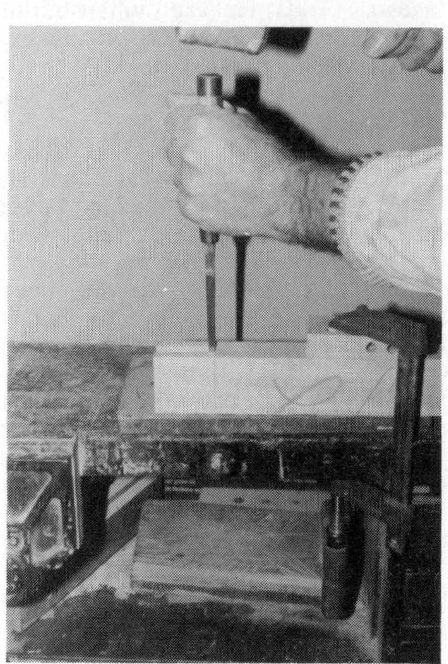

then the member fitting into the trenches can have its slotted end forced outwards.

The slotted part of the joint has its sides cut with the tenon saw. Again, the method and sequence of working are the same as cutting down the grain for a half lap joint. Always keep the wood as low as possible in the vice, work from both edges, and cut with the saw just touching the line on the waste side of it.

The bulk of the waste from between the kerfs is now removed with either a coping saw or a bow saw. However, neither of these saws can be used with the same accuracy as the tenon saw, and therefore the sawing is deliberately made about 1–3 mm (1/16 in.–1/8 in.) away from the line. The remaining waste is trimmed back to the line by chisel. For this part of the cutting, the wood should be secured to the top of the bench with a G-cramp, and a chisel selected which is as close a fit within the slot as possible. Chiselling is carried out half way from each edge, with the flat side of the chisel against the line. Test the flatness of this chiselling, too, to ensure there is no roundness which would prevent a good fit.

An alternative method of removing the waste is to combine the use of the tenon saw with a brace and bit, or equivalent. A single hole is bored at the lower end of the slot, with a chisel being used for the final trimming. This is especially useful where the size of the wood is such as to make cutting with a narrow bladed saw difficult. Suitable measures must be taken when boring to ensure that splintering on the exit side of the hole is avoided.

CUTTING BY BANDSAW

The slotted part of the joint can be formed on the bandsaw, or partly so. Where the slot is cut from edge to edge on the wood, and this is fairly wide compared with its thickness, then with most small bandsaws it may be necessary to extend the height of the rip fence. The fence must be checked to ensure it is square in the vertical plane to the table and, therefore, parallel to the blade. Checks must also be made to the saw guides to ensure the blade is running true with minimal side play. Even slight inaccuracies on the adjustments of the bandsaw can result in these being reflected in the accuracy of the cut, and it only takes a small discrepancy to result in a poorly-fitting joint.

When cutting any kind of joint, a wide blade should be fitted to the machine, one over 13 mm (1/2 in.) wide is preferred. For straight sawing, a wider blade will give more accurate cutting than a narrow one. The teeth of the blade must also be in good condition. Teeth of bandsaw blades often wear, or are blunted, more on one side than the other, and such a blade has a tendency to wander slightly off course.

Great care is needed in the setting of the fence when using this method of cutting the joint. This is because, should the cut be made so as to produce a joint which is too tight, it is very difficult for the bandsaw to remove a fractional amount of wood – the blade tends to ride over the surface from the previous cut. For this reason, when using a band-

Fig. 38 *Sawing along the grain with the bandsaw.*

saw to form the slots, cut these first and then make the fine adjustments to the trenches to provide a satisfactory joint.

Only the sides of the slot can be cut on the bandsaw. Cutting across the grain at the end of the slot has to be completed by one of the methods suggested for forming the joint entirely by hand. While it would be possible to remove all the waste from the slot by taking several passes adjusting the fence a little each time, the reality is that this would be very slow and the waste could be removed quicker by alternative methods. It is also technically possible to cut the ends of the trench on the bandsaw, by using the cross cut fence. It would, however, be very difficult to gain sufficient precision so as to produce good fitting joints. Where joints are cut on the bandsaw, use can be made of stops to limit the extent of the cut, and these can be secured to either the fence, or the top of the table.

USING THE CIRCULAR SAW

Cuts along the grain as required for forming the slot for the bridle, as well as other joints including tenons and some half laps, can be made on the circular saw bench. A simple home-made jig needs to be constructed from 19 mm (¾ in.) blockboard or similar, to which the workpiece can be cramped in the vertical position. The blade is set to project above the table by an amount equal to the extent of the slot, and the rip fence set accordingly to guide the jig. Note that the fence must be sufficiently long to provide support for the jig until the wood is well clear of the rear of the blade once the cut is completed. The usual crown guard to the saw cannot be employed when this jig is in use, and therefore alternative methods of protection must be provided to the side of the blade.

One limitation of cutting down the grain in the way just described is the length of wood which can reasonably be supported and held. If it is too long or too heavy, then difficulty will be experienced in maintaining proper control and therefore safety. The question of size of workpiece which can safely be moved under control on small-sized machines is one which has to be kept in mind at all times, whatever the machine and whatever operation is being carried out.

THE POWER MORTISER

Both square chisel mortisers, and slot mortisers, can be used for cutting the slot of the bridle joint. Certain heavy duty drill stands, including the Record Ridgway model and that from Jarrett and Son are provided with mortising facilities and accept square chisels, in both cases up to a maximum of ½ in. The chisel determines the width of this part of the joint; and this should be cut first and the trenches made to suit.

Only fairly small amounts can be removed at a time with a drill powered mortiser, especially in hardwoods. The cut should be started at the base of the slot, to ensure the end of the cut is true. If only a 'part cut' is made at the end of the slot, the wood can move slightly, and the result will be a sloping, or rounded, surface at the base. In addition, by starting at the base of the slot rather than the end of the wood, there is less chance of the wood to the sides of the slot being forced outwards, which again would result in inaccuracy. Where a cut from a mortise chisel is required to be made completely through the wood, then the cut should be made half way or thereabouts from each edge.

A popular type of slot mortiser is that which is a part of a combination machine, or an attachment for a planer/

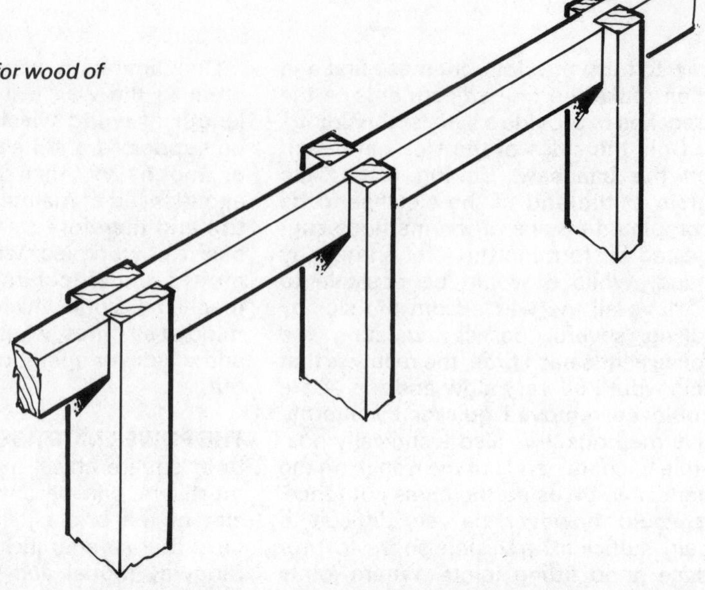

Fig. 39 *Bridle joints for wood of unequal sizes.*

thicknesser. Cutters for slot mortisers are readily available in both imperial and metric diameters and, while most operate while rotating clockwise, certain machines require a cutter to operate in an anti-clockwise direction.

Slot mortise cutters are at their most efficient when light cuts are taken, especially the small diameters. Far less strain is imposed on the cutters if they are used primarily to bore out the waste, with sideways movement made to smooth the sides and remove irregularities. In addition to efficiency of cutting by concentrating on axial rather than lateral movement, waste removed by lateral movement can lead to possible inaccuracy in wood with irregular grain. This is because of the slight tendency of the mortise cutter to follow the grain, especially if the table to which the wood is secured is not totally rigid. As with the chisel mortiser, the cutting should be started at the line indicating the base of the slot, although some hand chiselling will always be required in order to 'square-off' the cut.

Other Variations of the Bridle
The main purpose of the trenches is to prevent lateral movement, and therefore fairly shallow trenches are normally adequate. Apart from where the material being jointed is especially large, the trenches are usually made around 3–6 mm (⅛ in.–¼ in.) deep. Even so, where the wood to be trenched is rather thin, then a trench can be formed on one side only. All other aspects of the joints remain the same.

Where the bridle is used for a framework which is rebated and moulded, then modification is needed in order to take account of the profiling to the inner edges. Where the moulding is traditionally carried out prior to assembly, then the wood on the slotted member has to be cut back level with the rebate, and the moulding mitred so as to meet in the corner. The moulding can also be formed by router after assembly in order to simplify the work and also create a rounded corner and with this, continuity of the moulding from one member to the other. In this case, the

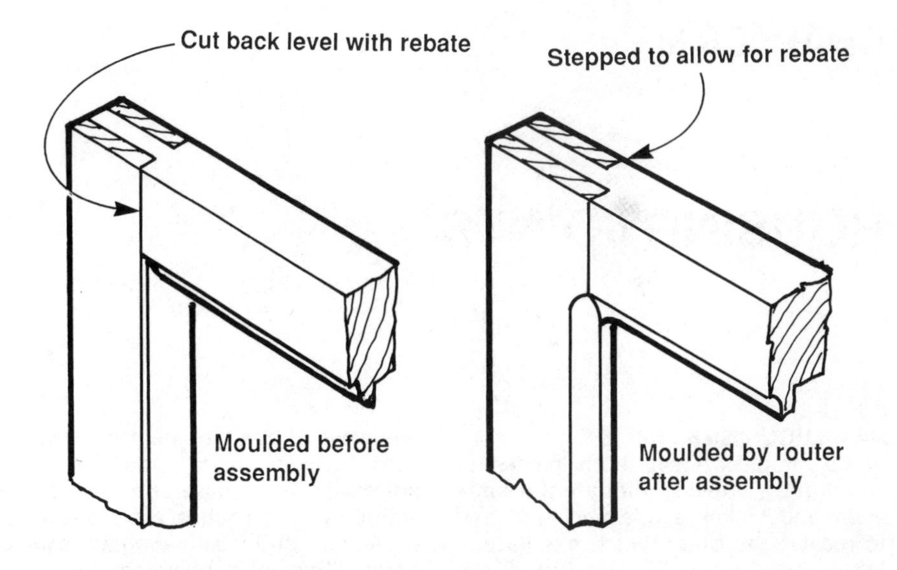

Fig. 40 *Corner bridles with moulded edges.*

component cut on its outer surfaces to create what is effectively a tenon has the extent of the two cuts differing from one side to the other by an extent equal to the depth of the rebate. This is so it will fit the 'stile' member accurately, whose rebate runs across the grain of the 'rail'. Note that the usual rule for sequence of working is to cut the joints before grooving, rebating, moulding, and making similar cuts.

Where appearance is particularly important, and it is desired to make the joint into something of a feature, then the trench can be made with tapered sides. This does not detract from the strength of the joint and adds visual interest, and can be employed where the faces of the two pieces are flush, or not. The tapering feature can be introduced onto both sides of the joint, or on the face only.

The bridle joint can also be formed where the trenches are not cut across the full width of the wood, and where they are 'stopped' in this way they would normally be made around two thirds of the width. The advantages of this variation are that strength is retained in the trenched member and the joint is fully concealed. The projecting ends of the slotted member can be chamfered to add to the neatness.

Use of the bridle joint can also be made for constructional assemblies, such as the brackets for external door porches. The diagonal brace is jointed at its ends by bridles which are both angled and stopped; this is typical joinery work which is carried out by hand.

CHAPTER 5

HOUSING JOINTS

BASIC HOUSINGS

In its simplest form, both pieces of wood in the housing joint are the same width and thickness, one piece trenched to receive the other which has its end left quite square. The depth of the trench is usually made one-third the thickness of the wood. Anything less provides minimal support, especially where the joint is used for supporting shelves, and a deeper trench would unnecessarily weaken the trenched component. The 'one-third rule' crops up quite frequently in woodworking, although it is by no means a rigid rule.

A word about terminology might be appropriate. Whereas a trench is made across the grain, a similar cut formed along the grain is known as a groove, regardless of the size of the cut in either case. The router will work efficiently regardless of the direction of the grain when using the same cutter. A 'straight' router cutter can be used for forming 'trenches' and 'grooves', and in fact straight cutters are often called grooving cutters.

In its basic form, the joint can be used for simple bookshelves, although one of the variations shown later would be preferred. Divisions of boxes are often trenched into the sides, as are cross-members of box-type plinths. Step ladders usually have housing joints employed for supporting the treads, although the trenches are made at an angle, and studded dividing walls incorporate housings between the main members. When used for constructional purposes, the trenches are rarely made more than 13mm (½ in.) deep, even though this might be less than one third the thickness of the wood.

In cabinet and furniture making, the usual practice is to have joints either completely hidden, or alternatively, exposed, making them a feature of the design. For this reason, the simple housing is not usually used for furniture, and one way of making a little feature of the joint, as for example on bookshelves, is to make the shelf rather wider than the trenched component, with the projecting front rounded over at the corners. The back of such a piece of furniture would probably be fitted into a rebate formed in the rear edges of the vertical members and does not affect the housings in any way, except that the shelves are made narrower by an amount equal to the thickness of the back.

Where you want to make the joint completely hidden from the front, as

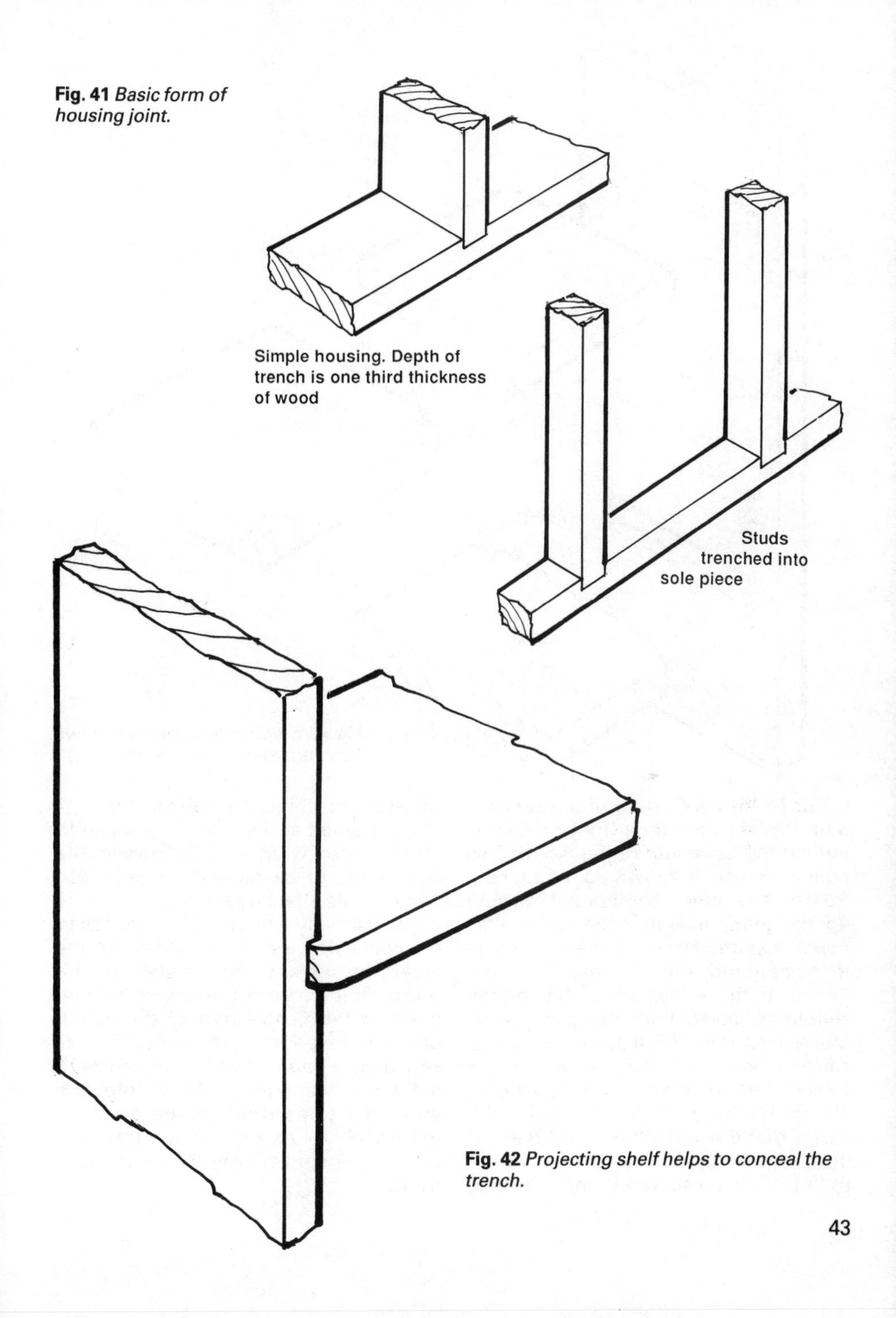

Fig. 41 *Basic form of housing joint.*

Fig. 42 *Projecting shelf helps to conceal the trench.*

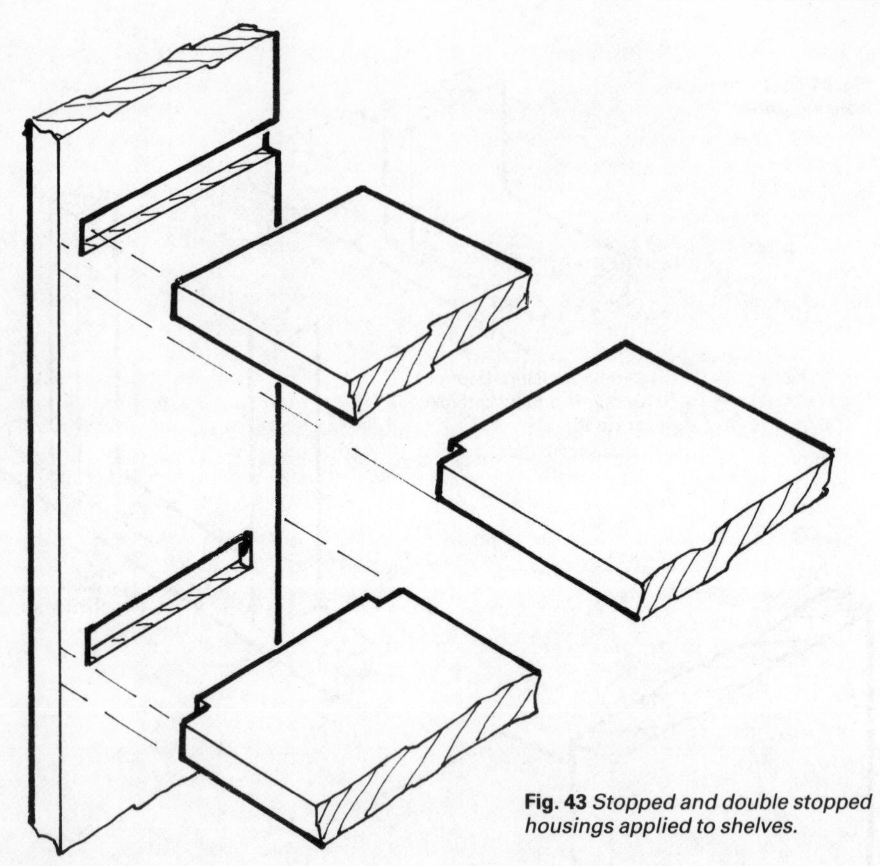

Fig. 43 *Stopped and double stopped housings applied to shelves.*

would be the case in a furniture carcase, then this is based on a trench which is not cut the full width of the wood. This type of trench is known as a 'stopped' trench. The other component making up the joint may then be made narrower than the trenched member so as to correspond with the extent of the trench. If the edges of all the pieces should be level, then the component fitting into the trench must be cut to correspond to the stopped part of the trench. For material which is around 16mm–19mm (⅝in.–¾ in.) thick, the extent of the wood left uncut at the end of the trench should be around 13mm (½ in.). Both these variations are used on shelved units and similar items. A shelf stepped at the front in order to fit into a stopped trench also allows for the front edge to be rounded or moulded without this affecting the fit.

Occasionally a housing joint needs to be concealed on both edges of the wood, for instance on the shelves of a room divider. Here the trench is confined to the centre part of the wood, being stopped at both ends. This is known as a double stopped trench, with the component to be fitted into this either the same width as the extent of the trench, or as wide as the trenched piece, in a similar way to the stopped trench.

CUTTING TRENCHES BY HAND

The marking out of the through trench is initially made by squaring across the wood in pencil, with the depth indicated by a gauge line on both edges. The stopped trench can only be gauged on one edge, with a gauge also used to indicate the limit of the trench on the face of the wood. The double stopped trench cannot have its depth indicated in any way, and again the gauge is used to indicate both points at which the trench is stopped.

Forming through trenches of the proportions required for housing joints is a little different from the techniques used for trenches which are cut on fairly narrow wood, as is usually the case for half laps. However, the cutting is started in the same way, by going over the pencil lines with a marking knife, restricting this to where waste is to be removed. The vee cut made on the waste side of the line is even more important on wide wood, and especially for those with limited experience. The vee cuts guide the saw, and the sawing is continued exactly down to the gauge lines. A useful dodge here is to cramp strips of wood to the blade of the saw. This is best done as follows: make the first cut without the guides, checking that the tips of the teeth are exactly touching the gauge lines on both edges of the wood. With the saw remaining at full depth in the kerf, secure the strips to the saw with their lower edges flush with the wood. This then allows all subsequent cutting to be made to exactly the same depth. The bulk of the waste is removed by chisel, using one which is as wide as reasonably possible within the trench. Cutting proceeds partly from each edge in turn. The hand router is a tool seen less and less in present-day tool catalogues, but is

Fig. 44 *Sawing edges of trench.*

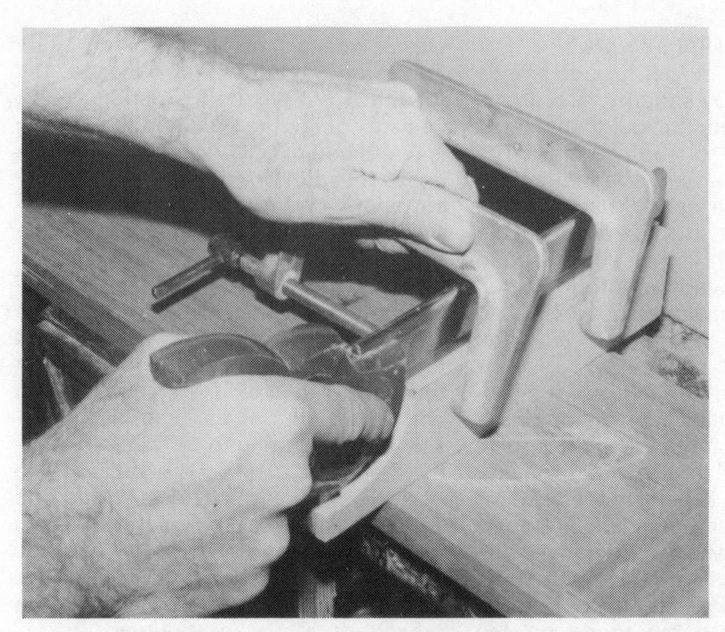

Fig. 45 *Depth stops added to tenon saw.*

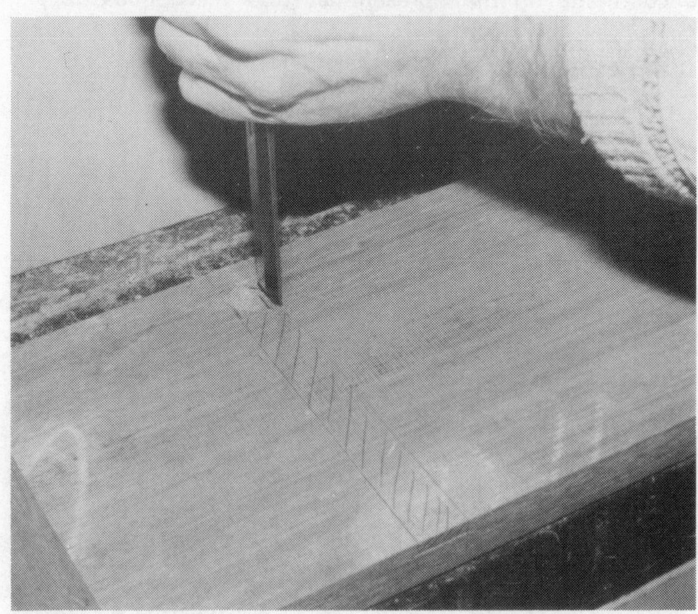

Fig. 46 *Chopping recess at end of stopped trench.*

Fig. 47 *The bulk of the waste is removed by chisel.*

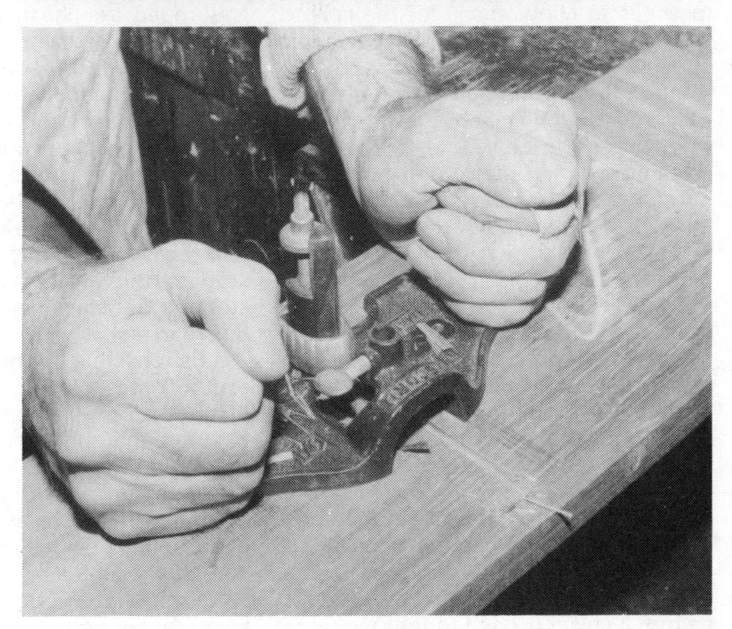

Fig. 48 *Levelling trench with hand router*

invaluable for the final levelling off of the trenches, and the wider the trench the more important this is. Routers are at their best when only light cuts are made with them, and properly used, will produce a trench with its lower surface flat and of uniform depth. Even so, it is always worth while checking the trench with a straight edge, especially if a router is not being used.

Cutting stopped trenches requires a different technique. The sides of the trench should have vee grooves formed as before, then the stopped end of the trench chopped out by chisel. This is done by chiselling the vee groove deeper and deeper, so that a small mortise or recess is formed. A little gentle chiselling across the grain helps to remove the waste, the aim being to make the depth of the recess equal to that of the trench. The purpose of the recess is to allow space for the saw to operate, although inevitably only short strokes can be taken. As with the through trench, the bulk of the waste is removed by chiselling but obviously from one edge only, and followed by levelling with a router. Where the piece fitting into the trench requires cutting at one corner so as to fit around the stopped end of the trench, this is carried out entirely by sawing.

Double stopped trenches have to be formed without the tenon saw. The sides of the trench are cut entirely by chisel, taking a series of vertical and sloping cuts until the required depth is reached making the whole of the length of the vee cuts deeper and larger. The depth has to be estimated, so it is wise to err on being too shallow in the early stages. In order to keep the sides of the trench as straight as possible, as wide a chisel as is available should be used. As before, a chisel is used to remove most of the waste. However, the chisel is used bevel side downwards, with the depth of cut controlled by the angle of the blade to the wood. Final levelling is by router, with the depth being checked by direct measuring.

USING THE RADIAL-ARM SAW

This is a very good method of forming the trenches for housing joints, and broadly follows the use of the radial-arm saw as described in Chapter 3. The method is at its best when using a dado cutter instead of the usual blade, but trenches can be formed just by using the blade. The advantages of the dado cutter include speed of working, and its precision. The packing washers included with the dado cutter allow for the width to be adjusted down to 0.1 mm, the cut made being dead parallel throughout, and the depth can be readily adjusted.

Stopped trenches can be largely formed on the radial-arm saw, but some chiselling will be required to complete the cut restricted by the curvature of the cutter. Because radial-arm saws have a tendency to advance forwards into the work once the cut is started, there is always a danger of the cut being made beyond the limit marked on the wood. This can be prevented by cramping a stop to the arm of the saw. Double stopped trenches cannot be formed on this machine.

It is possible to mount an electric router onto a radial-arm saw when using for forming trenches. It is essential that the router, the saw, and the bracket on to which the router is mounted are all properly matched; the set-up is similar to an overhead spindle. Stopped trenches can be cut in this way, as well as double stopped trenches, although for these the depth setting will have to be adjusted for each trench formed.

FORMING HOUSINGS ON THE CIRCULAR SAW

Again this is similar to the technique explained for the joints in Chapter 3, but there are limitations regarding the width of the wood. When the mitre fence is being used, accuracy of cutting tends to be reduced as the width of the wood increases. This is simply because of the limitations of a mitre fence which operates by sliding in a groove in the top of the table. Also, the distance from the front edge of the table to the edge of the blade restricts the width of wood which can be tackled. Saw benches which incorporate a sliding table for cross cutting purposes can cope with much wider wood, with far greater accuracy than can the mitre fence.

THE ELECTRIC ROUTER AND HOUSINGS

The router provides an ideal way of forming the trenches required for housings. However, the method is at its best when the diameter of the cutter used corresponds exactly to the width of trench required, simplifying the technique and giving a high level of accuracy. Straight cutters are available in small incremental sizes which makes matching the cutter to the width of trench straightforward, and the thickness of the wood can also be adjusted at the preparation stage to correspond with the router cutter.

The router needs a guide in order to control its movement across the wood. In its simplest form, this is made up in

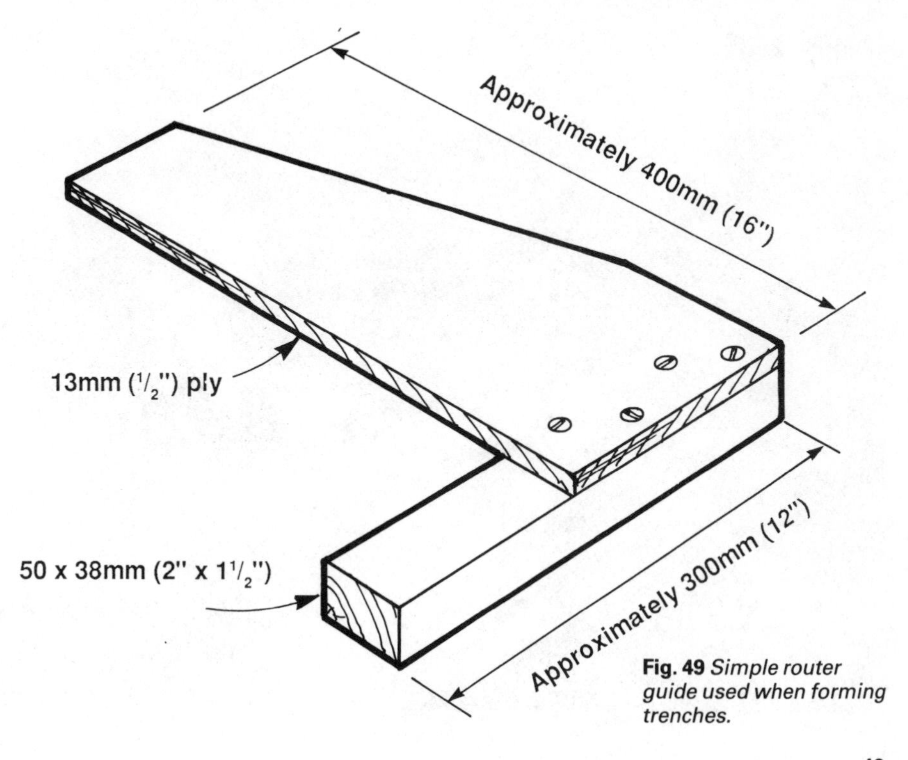

Fig. 49 *Simple router guide used when forming trenches.*

the workshop, following the principle of the T-square, and in use is cramped to the wood. This type of guide controls one edge of the base only, and therefore pressure has to be consciously maintained to ensure close contact between the router base and the guide. Remember too that cutter rotation will pull the tool against the guide in one direction and pull it away in the other. Always check first. With practice it works perfectly well, and allows for all three forms of housings to be prepared. A small amount of hand chiselling will be required at the ends of the cut so as to square them off. If preferred, a guide incorporating two arms can be made similar to that described for cutting half laps, which ensures better control as both edges of the router base are restrained within the guides.

A commercial version of the single-arm T-square is available, made by Wolfcraft known as the Combinal. It has its own cramp at the 'stock' end, but it is wise to also cramp the end of the arm to the wood to ensure total accuracy. The Combinal can be adjusted to give angles other than right angles, and can also be used for other applications such as guiding a jig saw, or portable circular saw.

A router guide device known as a

Fig. 50 *Trenching with the router and simple home made jig.*

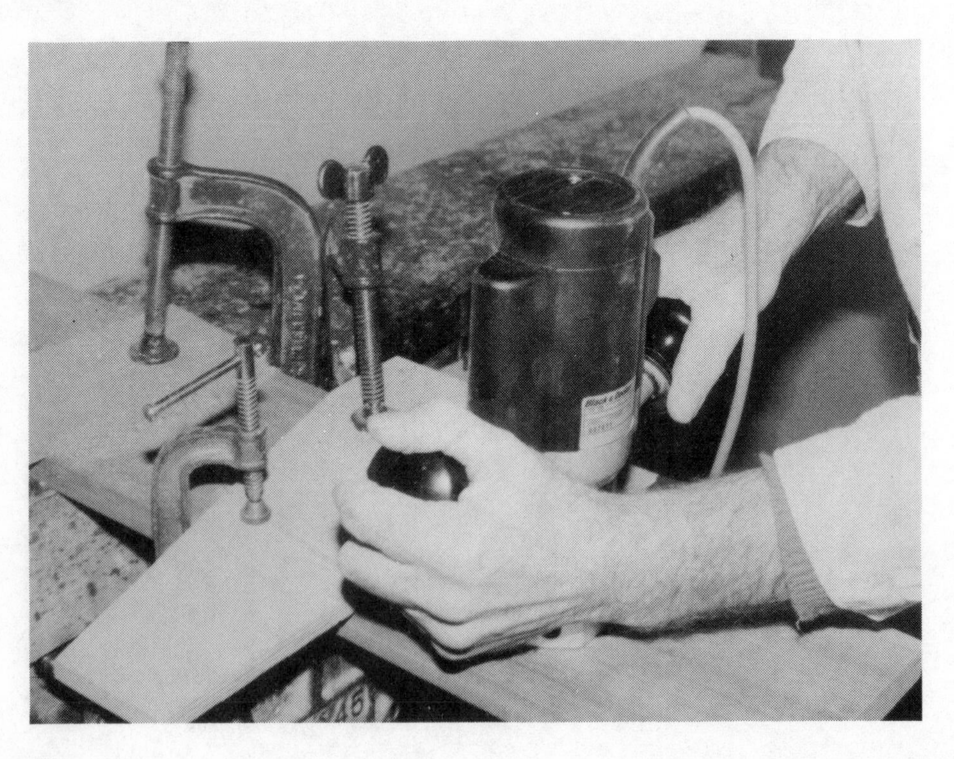

tracking fence is made by Trend Machinery and Cutting Tools Ltd, who are specialists in router cutters, as well as other products. Although designed specifically for Elu routers, a universal sub-base is also available enabling other makes of router to be used with the fence. The essence of this piece of equipment is a hard plastic fence, accurately grooved to accommodate a duralium bar which is mounted by blocks to the base of the router. There is no 'stock' to the main fence, this has to be positioned on the wood to suit the nature of the cut being made and secured by G-cramps. The equipment allows for the router to move freely forwards and backwards along the track, with no sideways movement therefore giving total control and accuracy. The fence can be cramped to the work at any angle, but this must be established and checked by the user first.

In all cases where any of the above router guides are in use, the guide must be secured to the work some distance from the position where the housing is required. This distance will depend on the size of the router base, and the diameter of the cutter. This can usually be established by direct measuring, but making a trial cut in waste material is always worth while.

Fig. 51 *Using the Trend router guide system.*

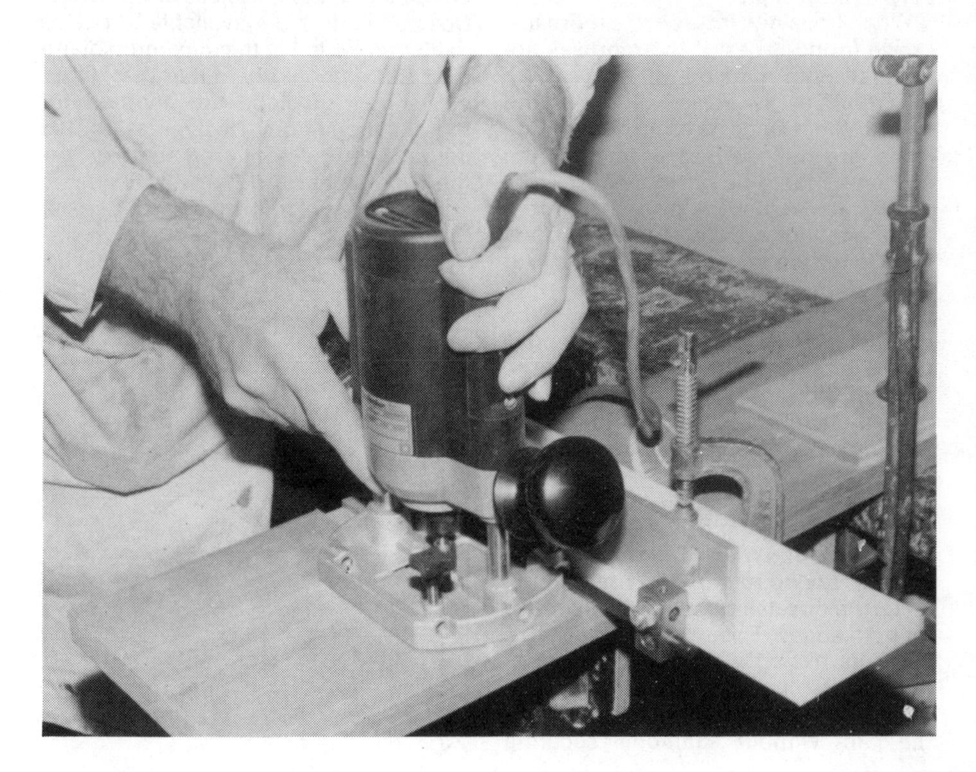

Other Variations of the Housing Joint

Where considerable strength is required in the joint, the housing can be combined with mortises and tenons. Two or more mortises are normally incorporated, depending on the width of the wood. As the thickness of the wood on which housings are formed is likely to be fairly limited, and this effectively reduced further by the trench itself, any mortises forming part of the joint are almost certain to be cut to the full thickness of the wood. This means the ends of the tenons will be visible on the outer surfaces when the work is assembled and it is not, therefore, a joint likely to be adopted on furniture unless visible joints are intended to be a part of the design.

When housings incorporate mortises, I have found it best if the mortises are cut first. Both marking out and cutting the mortices is easier if completed before the trench is cut. Where the joints are intended as a feature, the mortises should be positioned symmetrically across the width of the wood, and the tenons are usually wedged. Not only do the wedges increase the locking effect of the joint, they also improve the fit and thus the appearance. The wedges may be driven in at the edges of the tenons so as to be across the grain of the mortised member, or positioned diagonally. There is more information on mortise and tenons in the next chapter.

Another variation of the housing used where extra strength is needed is the dovetail form. Where the wood is fairly narrow, say up to around 76 mm (3 in.) wide, the dovetail slope is usually made on both edges. This type of joint can be used, for example, on the upper cross-rails of the underframing of a small table, where the mechanical strength of the joint without additional securing other than glue is considerable.

This joint can be formed by hand using saw and chisel, although a side rebate plane will be very useful for trimming purposes in order to gain a snug fit. Such a plane is no. 079 from the Stanley range. It has a blade at each end so can be used for left or right hand working, and is fitted with a depth gauge.

Once again the router provides a fairly simple way of cutting both parts of the joint, although a router table with a high fence is necessary for forming the component which fits into the trench. The aim should be to form the trench with a single pass of the router, and therefore the size of the cutter must be related to the thickness of the wood. Dovetail cutters are available to cut up to 22 mm (⅞ in.) at the maximum diameter, but it should be noted that different angles of slope are adopted for these cutters from 95 degrees to 105 degrees. It is essential, therefore, that the same cutter, or one with the same angle, be used for forming both parts of the joint.

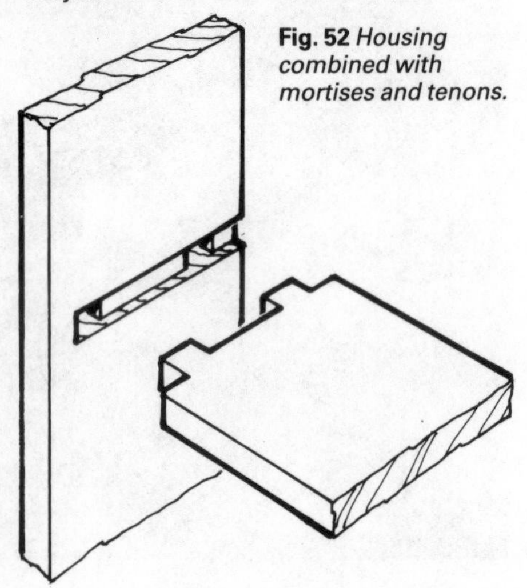

Fig. 52 *Housing combined with mortises and tenons.*

Fig. 53 *Removing waste between tenons.*

Where the wood is relatively wide, as is the case with bookshelves and similar constructions, then the dovetail slope is normally restricted to one edge. It is also usual to make the trench taper in width. The wider the wood, the more is gained from the tapering nature of the joint. It is very much easier to attain a good tight fit where the joint tapers, than would be the case if the edges were parallel. Properly prepared, this joint is highly effective as the further the

Fig. 54 *Dovetail housings.*

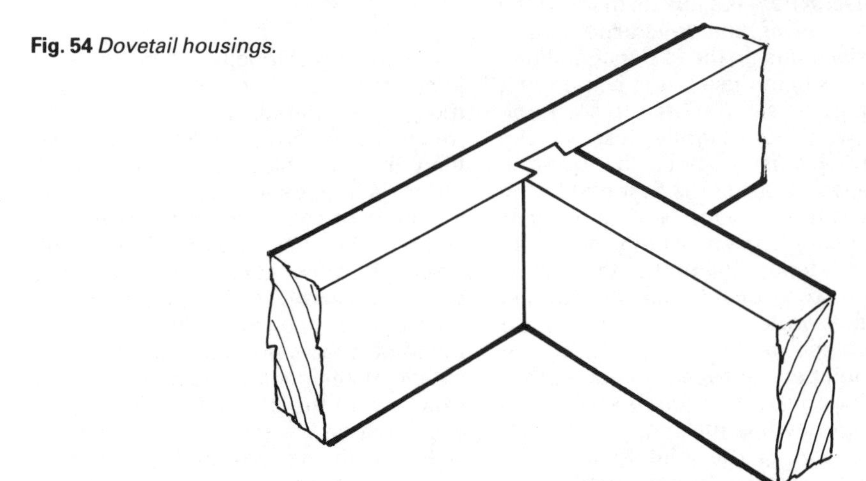

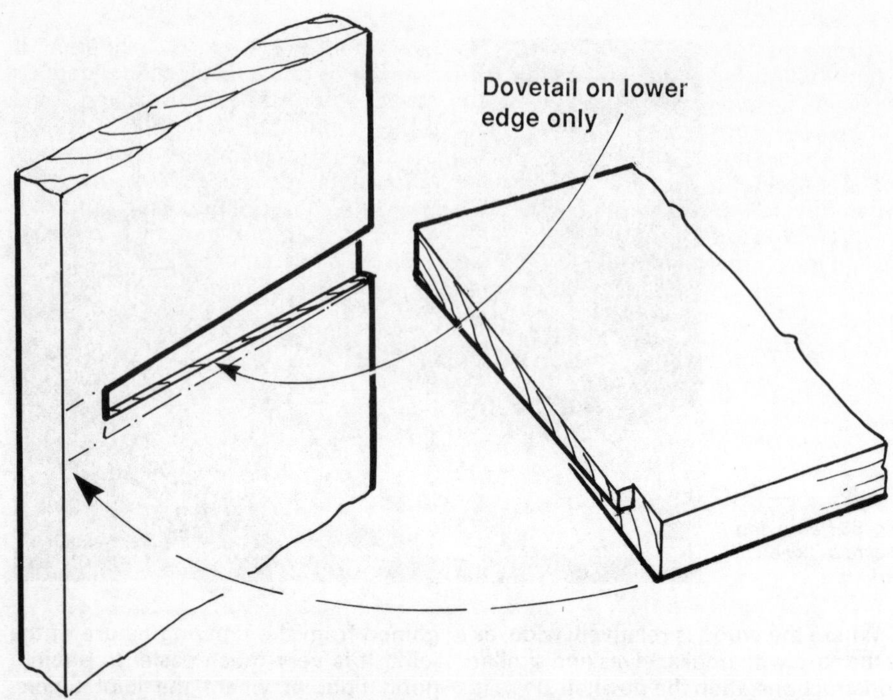

Fig. 55 *Dovetail housing as applied to shelves.*

component enters the trenched member, the more the two parts are pulled together and the tighter the joint becomes. Where the joint is made at the ends of shelves, the dovetailed feature is usually made on the underside. When a router is being used, it is best to first cut a parallel sided trench to the minimum width or slightly less of the trench. This is followed by using a dovetailed cutter so as to provide the undercut to one edge, with the router guide being angled slightly so as to create the taper. The end of the corresponding component can be formed with the router, but only partly so unless a special jig is made. Except for large numbers of repeat joints, such a jig of the accuracy required would hardly be worthwhile making, so completing this part of the joint to form the taper is best tackled by hand methods.

I have occasionally seen housing joints formed where the end of one member is rebated, or stepped, with the trench made correspondingly narrower than the full thickness of the wood. There is really no advantage in this variation of joint compared with one without the step feature. There are, however, drawbacks, apart from the extra work involved. The piece which is normally the shelf is weakened, and for the joint to be satisfactory in its fit, the extent of the rebate must correspond exactly with the depth of the trench, as any variation will result in a joint which does not fit properly and is therefore further weakened.

Securing the Joint

Even though nails and pins can be punched in and a filler used to help conceal their positions, the fewer pins used on conspicuous surfaces the better. The best position for the pins is when driven in from the underside, but their exact location and angle require care, if they are to be fully effective. This technique can only be properly carried out while the work is fully held in cramps, or has already been glued. On furniture work, nailing housing joints through the outer surface is a sure sign of a lack of knowledge and experience.

Dovetail housings should not require pinning, glue alone is sufficient. Cramps, though, always help to ensure a joint is fully home.

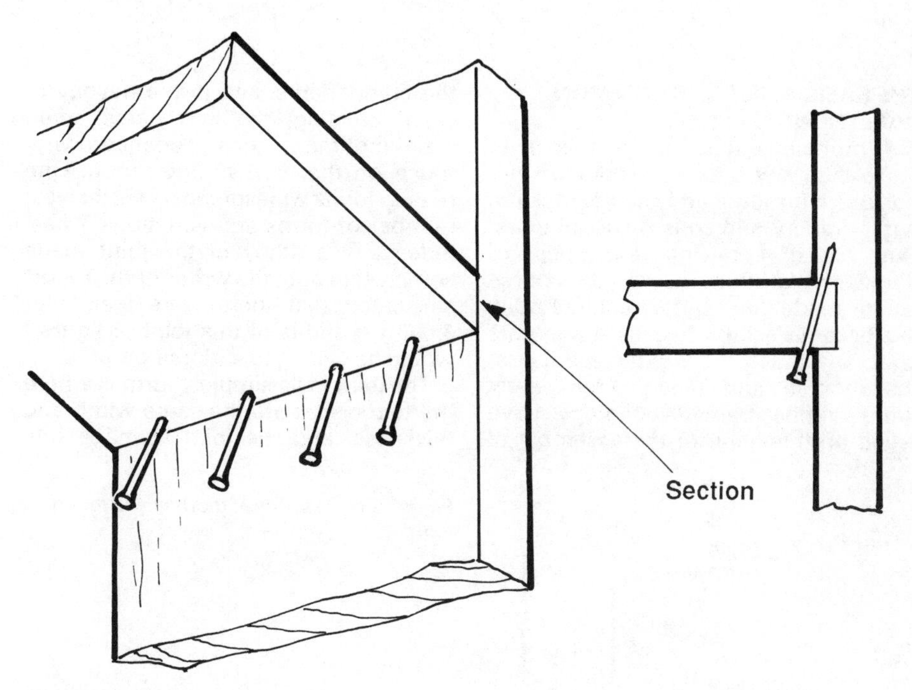

Fig. 56 *Secret nailing of housing joint.*

CHAPTER 6

THE MORTISE AND TENON

THE BASIC JOINT AND COMMON VARIATIONS

The mortise and tenon joint is used more than any other in woodworking, not just in furniture and cabinet making, but in joinery and constructional work. Our oldest surviving examples of domestic furniture were of course 'joiner made' long before cabinet making became established as a separate craft, and these show extensive use of the mortise and tenon. From early times, timber-framed buildings have relied on this joint for the assembly of the components, and in the heyday of canal building, the lock gates, often weighing many tons, depended very much on the mortise and tenon. One reason for its widespread use is the vast number of forms and variations it has. Indeed, in a study of the joint made some years ago, the writer of the report calculated that there were well over 3,000 variations of this joint, a figure I would be willing to endorse.

The joint in its simplest form is where the two pieces are the same width and thickness, and the joint is made one

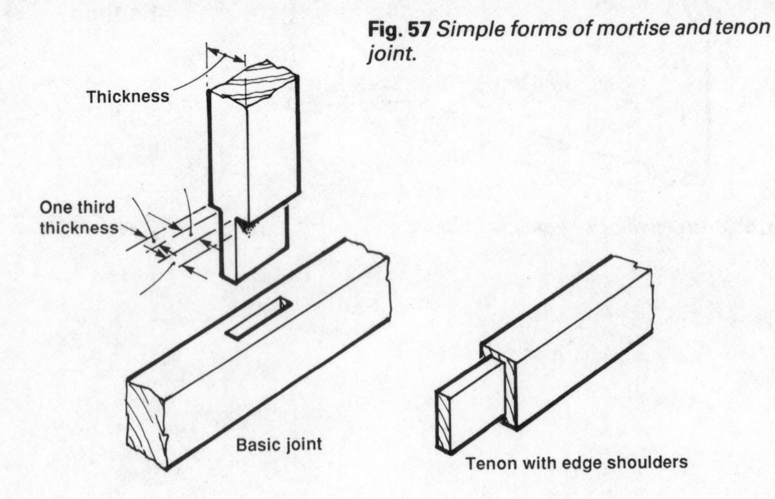

Fig. 57 *Simple forms of mortise and tenon joint.*

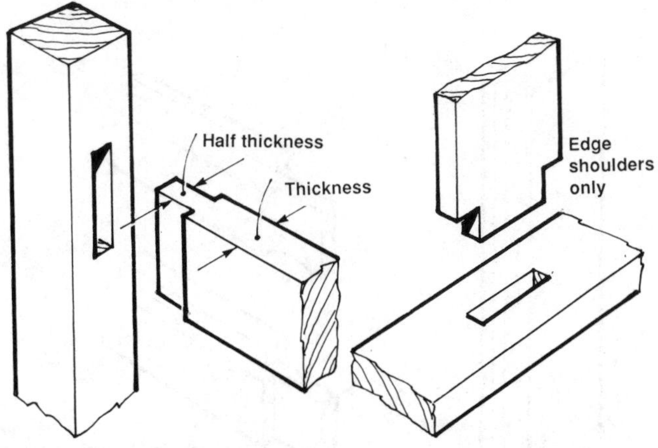

Fig. 58 *Joints in wood of different sizes.*

third the thickness of the wood. Where the thickness does not readily divide by three, then the joint is made slightly more than a third. For example, if the wood is 22 mm (⅞ in.) thick, the joint should be made 8 mm (5⁄16 in.). This is because the tenon tends to be the weaker part of the joint as far more wood is cut away as waste, and therefore a stronger joint results if the thickness of the tenon is increased. Where the mortise is cut to pass completely through the wood it is known as a 'through' joint, and where it is formed only part way into the wood is called a 'blind', or 'stopped', joint.

In furniture work, as distinct from joinery, it is a common practice to form small 'edge' shoulders on the tenons. The extent of these edge shoulders is normally about 3 mm (⅛ in.). These give a neater joint once assembled, as the ends of the mortise are completely hidden. It also means, in the case of fairly wide members, that should there be even very slight shrinkage, the mortise does not become exposed.

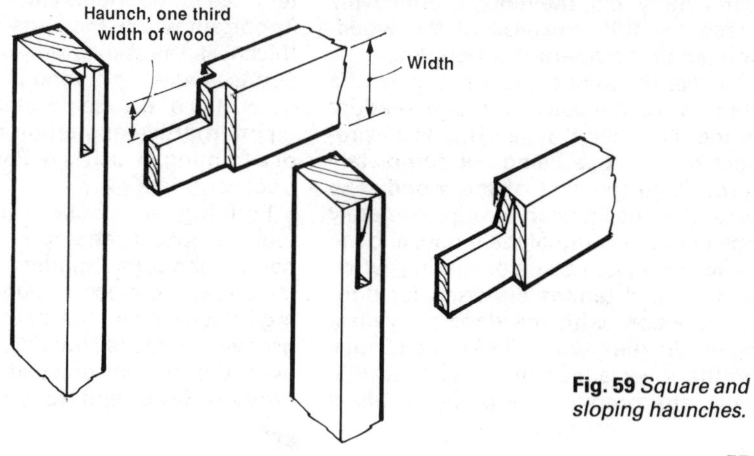

Fig. 59 *Square and sloping haunches.*

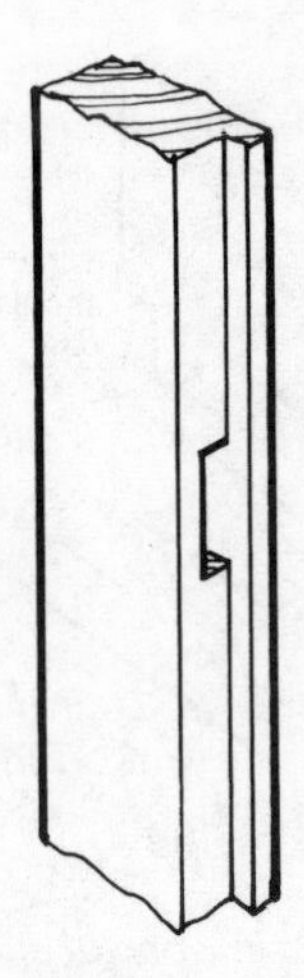

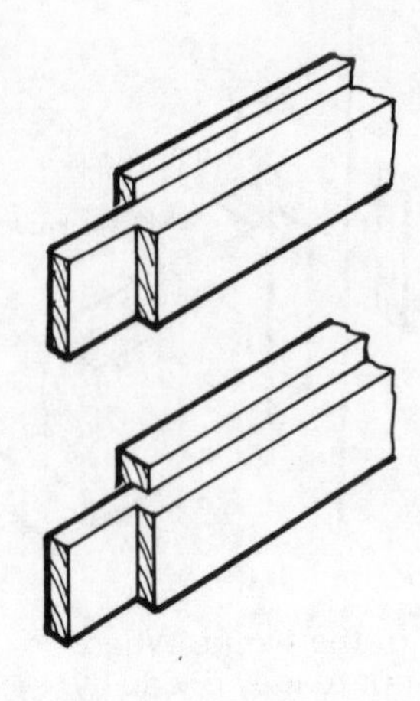

Fig. 60 *Long and short shoulders to tenons.*

It is often the case that the piece being tenoned is rather thinner than the component to be mortised, such as the legs and rails of a table. As the tenon is the weaker part of the joint, increasing its thickness means a stronger joint. Where the two parts are of different thickness, the tenon should be made approximately half the thickness of the tenoned member. If the difference in sizes between the two pieces is quite considerable, with the tenoned member particularly thin, the tenon is effectively made the full thickness of the wood, with edge shoulders only adopted.

Where the joint forms the corner of a framework, the usual variation to adopt is the 'haunched' type. This is to prevent the mortise being cut completely through to the end of the wood. The extent of the haunch is approximately one third the width of the tenon, and the haunch may be square or sloping. Often mortise and tenons are used for door construction, with the door carrying a panel. As the panel is held in a groove on the inner edges of the door framework, the grooves are going to affect the joint. This is because it is generally very much easier to form the groove from end to end, and then adapt the joint to suit the grooves. Here the haunch serves to fill the outer end of the groove. Note that the inside edge of the tenon has to be adjusted to allow for the groove.

The whole purpose of the haunch, whether square or sloping, is to provide some support within the mortised member for the full width of the tenoned component. This is particularly important where the parts are the same thickness, as maximum support helps surfaces adjacent to the joint to remain flush. It is of course possible to form an 'open' mortise and tenon at the corner of a framing, which is really the same as a corner bridle.

Forming a stopped groove is a tedious job if attempted entirely by hand, although modern equipment, including the electric router and rebating attachments, make cutting stopped grooves far more straightforward. However, the normal practice is to cut the grooves from end to end, and then adopt square haunches.

A common variation of the mortise and tenon is the one known as the 'long-and-short-shoulder'. This is used where the material has a rebate formed in it, and again is frequently used on door and frame construction where glass is to be incorporated. The extent of the rebate often encroaches on the tenon, and therefore the tenon has to be adjusted in width to allow for this. This variation gets its name from the staggered arrangement of the shoulders, the difference between the two being equal to the depth of the rebate.

A barefaced tenon is a tenon with a shoulder formed on one side only, and a typical application of this joint is between the legs and rails of a table. Where the outer surfaces of the legs and rails need to be flush, using the barefaced tenon will mean the mortise is not too near the edge of the leg and thus maximum strength is achieved.

Often two rails are tenoned at right angles into one leg, as is the case of the table mentioned above. The mortises are usually cut from adjoining surfaces until they meet, and then the ends of the tenons mitred so that each is of its maximum length. Note that where the outer surfaces are not wanted to be flush, the rails are often positioned off centre. This is an arrangement which enables the tenons to be as long as possible, as depth of joint adds to its strength. The mitred ends of the tenons should be just clear of one another to prevent possible fouling. This also applies with all stopped mortises, where the ends of the tenons must be given a little clearance.

Table legs and similar components that have rails jointed to them from two faces are by no means always square in section. One tenon is going to be longer than the other, so there is no point in mitring the ends and they are left square and just clear of one another. From both a practical and appearance point of view, the height of the lower rails on the legs of stools, tables, chairs and similar constructions is often staggered. This also allows for the tenons on all members to be of the maximum length.

Where a piece being tenoned is quite wide, the tenon is subdivided into two smaller tenons with a haunch between. The reason for this lies in the mortised

Fig. 61 *Section through legs showing mitred tenons.*

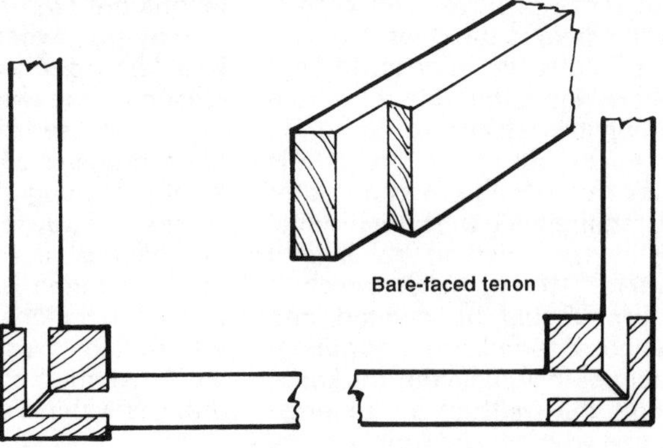

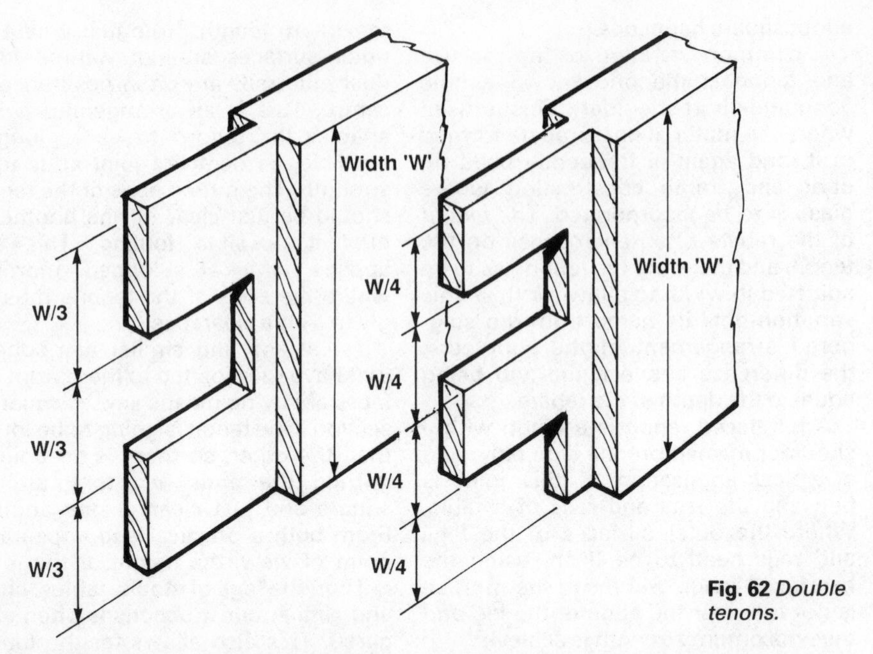

Fig. 62 *Double tenons.*

member. If a very long mortise was to be formed, this would considerably weaken this member, with the wood adjoining the mortise likely to be distorted. By leaving a little wood uncut in the centre of what would otherwise be a long mortise, strength is retained. In addition, this makes securing the joint easier and more positive. The correct name for this joint is the double tenon, sometimes incorrectly referred to as a forked tenon. Again the 'one-third' rule normally applies, relating to the tenon and the haunch, but where this joint is at the corner of a frame then an outer haunch is required and thus the original width of the tenon would be divided into quarters. The point at which a single tenon should be divided into double tenons depends on a combination of factors, including the thickness of the wood, the width of the tenoned member, and whether the mortises are through or stopped. As a general rule, though, the length of a mortise is not normally more than eight times its width. For furniture work, tenons on rails more than around 115 mm (4.½ in.) will have to be considered as double tenons.

Not to be confused with double tenons are twin tenons. These are cut side by side, whereas the double tenon is a large one subdivided. Again the reason for the twin tenon is to be found in the mortised part. With rare exceptions, mortises are formed so that their length is along the grain, rather than across it. Twin tenons do not incorporate haunches. A typical application of the twin tenon is on the 'drawer rail' which is positioned beneath a drawer at the front of a carcase, although there are other methods of accommodating drawers within a carcase.

Forming the Tenon by Hand

Marking out of the tenon follows the general rules already given, that is the shoulder is first marked by pencil, and then gone over with a marking knife. If first made with a marking knife, any corrections needed cannot be readily made. The expert with the tenon saw will usually be quite happy to saw a shoulder marked only in pencil, but the incision from the knife is more accurate and provides a sharper corner to the shoulder. As with other joints already discussed, vee cuts should be made at the shoulders to act as positive guides for the saw, and even competent craftsmen will consider this stage worthwhile on wide material.

The thickness of the tenon is marked with the mortise gauge. It helps if the pins are set directly to correspond to the width of chisel being used for the mortise; this helps both ease of cutting of the mortise, and accuracy of the joint. All the parts to be similarly jointed should be gauged at the marking out stage, and all lines should be checked as always.

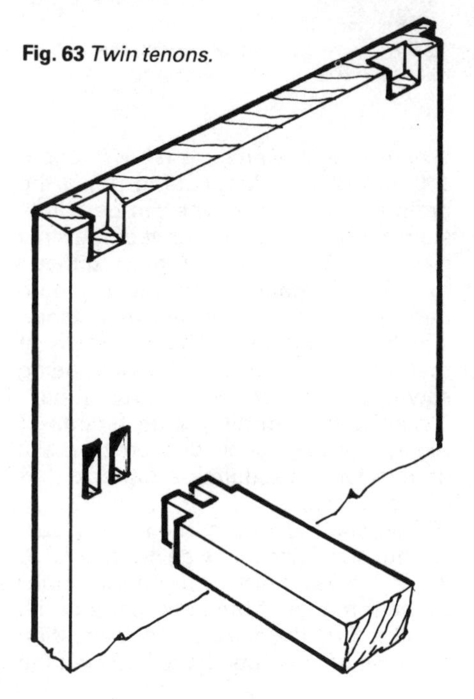

Fig. 63 *Twin tenons.*

Tenons are sawn with the tenon saw, and when cutting the shoulders in particular, the depth of the kerf must be accurately controlled, as sawing past the gauge line means the tenon is being weakened at its most vulnerable point. If the mortise and tenon joint fails because the tenon snaps off, the fracture is almost always adjacent to the shoulder.

Sawing down the grain for a tenon is exactly the same as for half laps, and bridle joints. The main points to remember are to keep the wood low in the vice, work partly from one side and partly from the other, and saw on the waste side of the line but so as to just touch it. If the waste alongside the cheek is not freed when the second cut is made, examine the wood to see where further sawing is needed.

Tenons are rarely left at their full width, the edges usually need cutting to form edge shoulders or haunches. My method of marking these is to use an ordinary marking gauge to make the lines along the grain, and a pencil to mark the projection of the haunch. This line is best made if a piece of wood of suitable thickness is held against the shoulder, and a pencil drawn along this. If a square haunch is being adopted but the mortised member is not grooved, then the projection of the haunch should be made about equal to its thickness. Remove the marked waste by sawing.

The above procedure for cutting tenons is the one I normally follow when working by hand, and it hardly

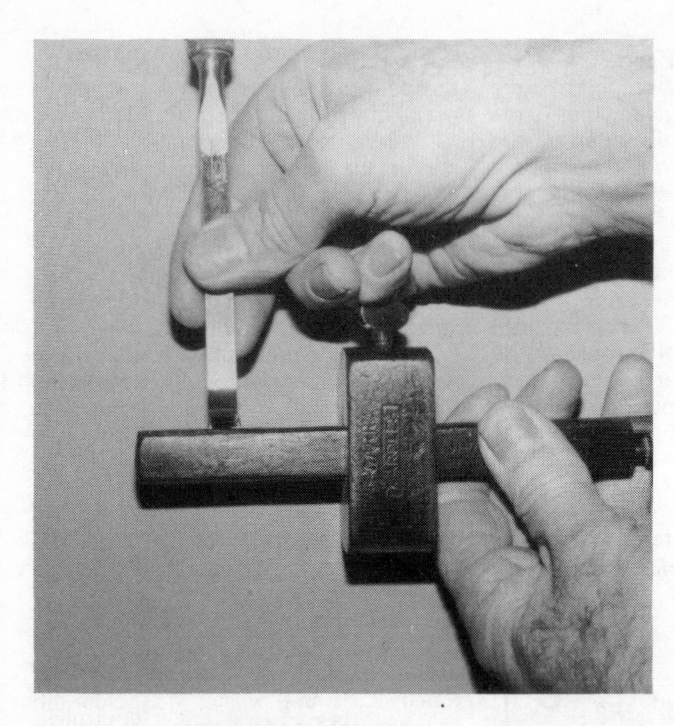

Fig. 64 *Setting the mortise gauge.*

matters whether the shoulder or the cheek is sawn first. The essence is to saw up to the lines, no more and no less. However, some craftsmen prefer to adopt a different sequence of sawing when forming a tenon. The advantage of this method is that all the marking out can be completed at the outset, the drawback is that more actual sawing is needed.

Where the tenons meet at right angles within the leg, the ends in most cases are mitred as described earlier in this chapter. This mitring is normally the last stage in the preparation of the joint, and is best cut with the aid of a mitre box, or block.

Cutting wide tenons is theoretically the same as on narrow wood, but in practice it presents some difficulties. Where the material is above about 100 mm (4 in.) wide, cutting down the grain to form the tenons can be a little slow and tedious. The result of the slow sawing is that it is much more difficult to follow the gauge lines, and any wandering of the saw results in a tenon which is inaccurate. The condition of the saw, the species of wood being sawn, and expertise all play a part. Nevertheless, forming wide tenons of the type likely to be divided to make double tenons requires a rather different approach.

One method I have found very successful for forming wide tenons is to 'trench' away most of the waste, prior to the removal of the outer parts of the cheeks. First the shoulder is sawn, then a couple of saw cuts made between the

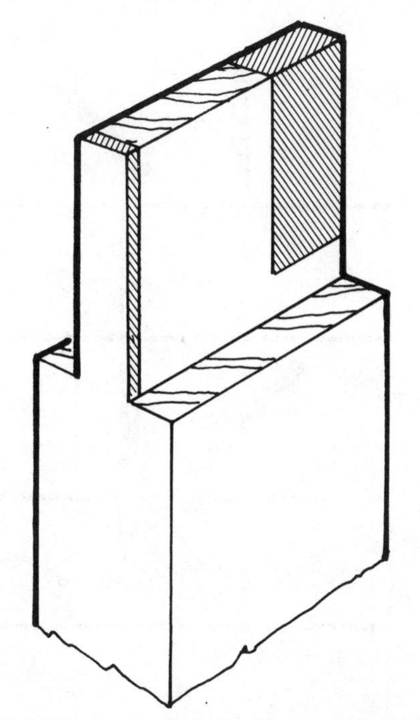

Fig. 65 *Tenon marked for edge shoulder and haunch.*

shoulder and the end of the wood. The exact positions are not important, and marking is not required. The bulk of the waste between the saw kerfs is then chiselled away, and the hand router brought into use to level off the trenches. The depth setting of the router is important, as this determines the thickness of the tenon. The remaining waste is simply planed away down to the gauge line.

Most wide tenons will be subdivided to form double tenons, and after first sawing down the grain with the back saw, the waste from the centre is cut away with either the bow or coping saw, then chiselled if this is needed.

Always check that the projection of the haunch is not greater than intended – if too long it will foul within the mortise and possibly cause gaps at the shoulders.

If the tenon does need slight trimming, a shoulder plane, or bullnose, is the best way of carrying this out. When used on the actual shoulder, a piece of scrap wood must be positioned at the end of the wood to ensure there is no splitting. This is best done by gripping both in the vice. Any easing must always be carried out with edge tools, never with a file or abrasive paper.

Cutting the Mortise by Hand

It is best to use a mortise chisel when the mortise is being formed by hand, and to ensure that the gauge lines correspond to the chisel being used. A correct approach at the outset promotes accuracy, simplifies the work, and goes a long way to eliminating the need for making 'adjustments' to the joint in order to arrive at a good fit. When a mortise is of the stopped type, it is essential for the depth of the chiselling to be accurately controlled. The best way to achieve this is to wrap masking tape around the blade at the appropriate distance from the cutting edge.

To speed up forming the mortise, it is better to start removing the waste by boring a series of holes. This should be done by using a bit which fits as closely as possible within the lines. To use a bit distinctly smaller than the mortise is far less effective. The first two holes should be made at the ends of the mortise adjacent to the lines, this again makes chiselling easier. With through mortises, this boring is best carried out part way from each edge of the wood.

For stopped mortises, the boring must be controlled in its depth. This can be done by using a standard depth stop if using a Jenning's type of bit, or by a wooden sleeve if using a short pattern

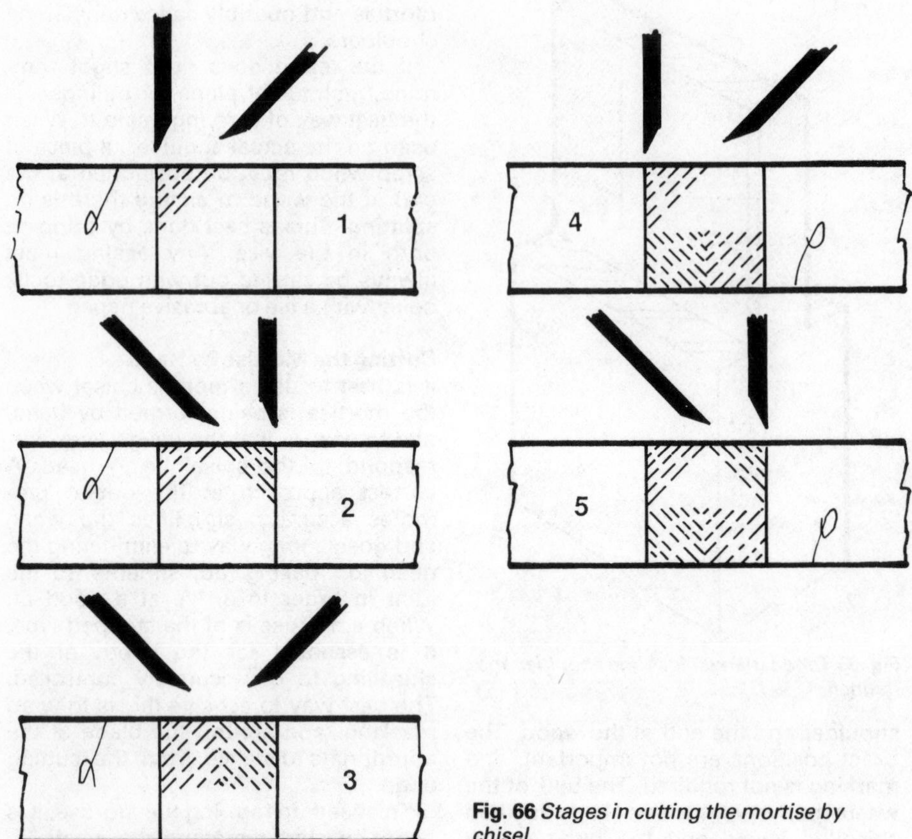

Fig. 66 *Stages in cutting the mortise by chisel.*

of bit. The holes should be made to the depth of the mortise, so that negligible chiselling is required on the bottom surface. Beware, though, of the point of the bit from penetrating the wood.

The mortise chisel is used for cutting across the grain, especially at the ends of the mortise, and a broad paring chisel to sever down the sides to remove the waste from between the holes. The paring chisel should be used with only the lightest of blows from the mallet, as heavy blows when the chisel is in line with the grain can quickly result in the wood being split. Through joints are chiselled from both edges, with the work fully supported on the underside. The work must be cramped to the bench with a chiselling board beneath the wood especially if it is a through joint. If held in a vice, pack beneath the wood and use the vice slides to avoid damage to the lower surface.

Special care is required at the end of the mortise. The cutting must be exactly up to the lines, and made with the chisel absolutely vertical. There is always some danger of sloping the chisel and thus producing a convex end, but this can be checked with a steel rule. Avoid using the chisel to lever the waste from the mortise, which would result in the corner at the end of the mortise being crushed and rounded over.

From time to time you will have to cut a mortise entirely by hand. For this, the whole of the chopping is carried out with the mortise chisel across the grain. A series of small cuts is the best method and two light blows from the mallet are far better than one heavy one. The aim is to remove the waste and not drive the chisel into the wood. When chopping the mortise it is better to keep the ends vertical from the outset, rather than cut the ends initially on the slope and then have the job of truing them up later.

Fig. 67 *Use of 'stop' when forming tenon on radial arm saw.*

As a guide to ensuring the chisel is vertical, a try square can be placed nearby on the bench. The chiselling is then done by sighting the chisel with the edge of the try square blade. This same method can be used when boring by hand. Remember that the chisel must be vertical in both directions, and when the sloping cuts are made, the chisel will remain vertical when viewed from the end of the wood.

Sloping haunches at the ends of the mortises are formed entirely by chisel simply by taking a series of cuts, until the required amount of waste has been removed. For square haunches made in wood which are not to be grooved, a tenon saw can be used to cut down the edges of the haunch before using the chisel to remove the waste, a small amount at a time.

Cutting Tenons using Power

The various methods suggested earlier for removing the waste at the ends of the wood for half laps and bridles can

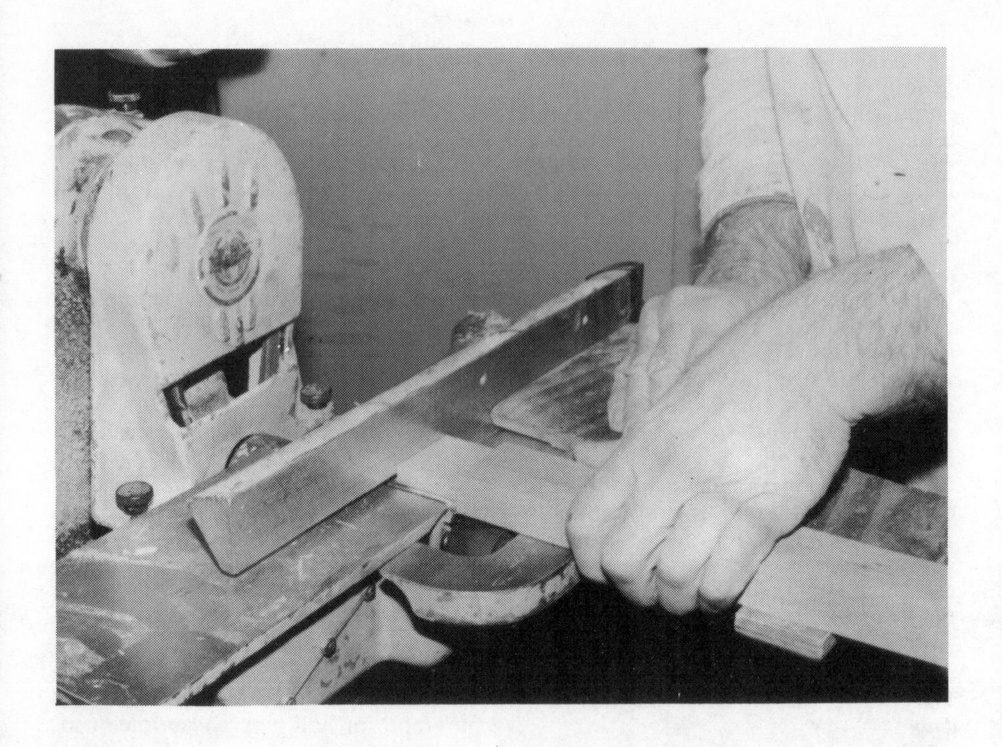

Fig. 68 *Using planer to cut small tenons.*

be used for forming tenons, including the circular saw, radial arm saw, router, and bandsaw. When using the bandsaw, it is preferable to have the cheek being sawn on the side of the blade further away from the fence, having first cut the shoulder. This allows for the waste to fall free of the blade. With all methods of cutting which take place from both sides, care is required when making any adjustments to the setting of the equipment being used. This is because the effect of the adjustment is double that which is actually made, assuming the tenon is in the centre of the wood.

The Power Mortiser

The square chisel mortise attachment, for use with a drill stand and power drill, forms an ideal way of cutting mortises. The wood has to be hand fed laterally as each cut is made, as distinct from a mortising machine where the sideways movement of the table and wood is controlled by wheel. Because of this, the setting of the work guides is critical, as the wood has to be free to slide but without any play. Wrap a piece of newspaper over the top and sides of the first piece to be mortised, and set the guides in close contact with the paper. When the paper is removed, there should be just the correct amount of clearance. Excess space will lead to considerable inaccuracy in the joint.

These mortising attachments are

suitable for mortises up to ½ in. wide. Where a wider mortise than this is needed, a second series of cuts can be made alongside the first. However, where this is done, the chisel used should be a half of the width of the mortise required, so that each series of cuts is being made fully into the wood. If a mortise chisel is used to make part cuts so as to widen a mortise, accuracy will be lost as the chisel will want to take the line of least resistance and drift partly into the space first made. This can also force the wood a little out of place within the guides.

When the chisel and bit are mounted in the stand, it is essential that a space of around 1.5 mm (1⁄16 in.) is left between the end of the bit, and the inside of the chisel. Fouling of the two will cause friction and burning. It is also essential that the 'window' in the chisel is facing left or right. This allows for better ejection of the chippings as the actual cuts are made. Chisels must be kept sharp, for which a special sharpening tool is needed that must match the size of chisel. Sharpening is done solely on the inner edges, never touching the outsides of the chisel.

As with the bridle, the first cuts should be at the ends of the mortise, and only light cuts made throughout. For blind mortises, the depth of cut can be controlled by the depth stop of the stand, and even for through joints this can be used, as the cutting should be made half way, or a little more, from each edge. The depth of haunches can also be controlled in this way. Where waste is left on the ends of the wood to

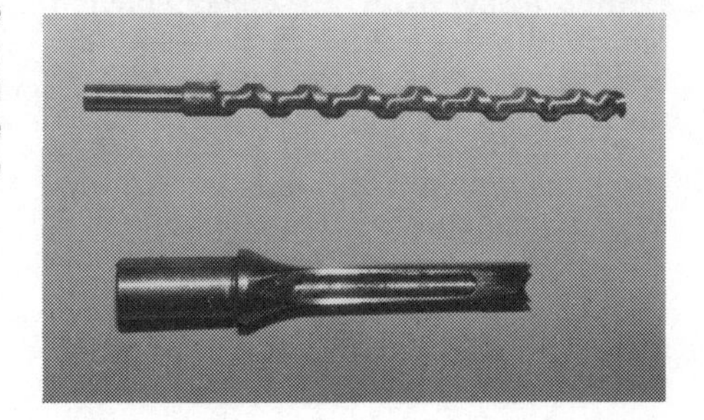

Fig. 69 *(top). Mortising on the heavy duty drill stand.*

Fig. 70 *(opposite). Hollow square chisel and bit.*

Fig. 71 *The slot mortiser in user.*

form joggles adjoining the mortises, the haunches can be cut into the joggles without any detriment. Always work with the face side, or face edge, facing the front, so that when it is turned over for completion, the same rule is followed and can be easily checked. Even when the mortise is in the centre of the wood, following a set pattern with the datum surfaces promotes accuracy, and is essential if a through mortise is off centre.

The same method used for slot mortisers discussed in Chapter 4 applies to mortises whether through or stopped. Long pieces of wood, when cramped at one end to the mortiser table, could well impose such a strain as to cause slight distortion of the table, and therefore minor inaccuracies in the cutting. If there is any danger of this, a temporary support should be arranged at the same height as the table, and thereby support the wood when the overhang is considerable. The question of support applies to many small machines where long work is being handled, and must be considered from the point of view of the accuracy of the cut being made, and the safety of the operator.

The rounded ends of the mortise produced by rotating cutters can be dealt with in two ways. Either the ends can be squared off by a chisel to produce the usual rectangular mortise, or the edges of the tenon can be radiused to match the mortise. Slot mortisers are very popular on the continent, where I understand that rounding the tenons is the usual practice. My own preference is to square off the mortise, which I believe gives a better joint and is easier to carry out.

Forming Mortises with the Router

The router provides a speedy and straightforward method of cutting mortises, particularly the smaller ones. The router is hand held, indeed router tables are of no help for this particular operation. However, for the person who is likely to carry out a lot of mortising with the router, a second fence for the tool is worth obtaining, providing that it is possible to fit one to both edges of the base. The use of two fences allows for the router to straddle the wood and thus when correctly adjusted, are both in contact with the wood, thereby offering full support. Routers are fast and efficient, but should be used principally by plunge action with lateral movement restricted to clean out the mortise. Non-plunge action routers cannot be used for forming mortises.

It is bad practice to expect a router to work beyond its reasonable capacity, especially relating to depth of cut followed by lateral movement. This can strain the bearings of the tool. It is also dangerous to gain extra depth of cut from the cutter by limiting its grip in the chuck – around 20 mm (¾ in.) of the shank should be inserted into the chuck for all operations. Long reach cutters are available, but should only be used with heavy duty routers.

The router can be used in the Wolfcraft 5005 Machining Centre to form mortises. This equipment will operate to high levels of efficiency and accuracy, readily controlled by the handwheels and the electronic read-out scales, whereby the movement of the table and the wood clamped to it is instantly displayed. This equipment is of special value for small scale work of a precise nature, but only certain routers can be fitted to the headstock.

Fig. 72 *Mortising with the router.*

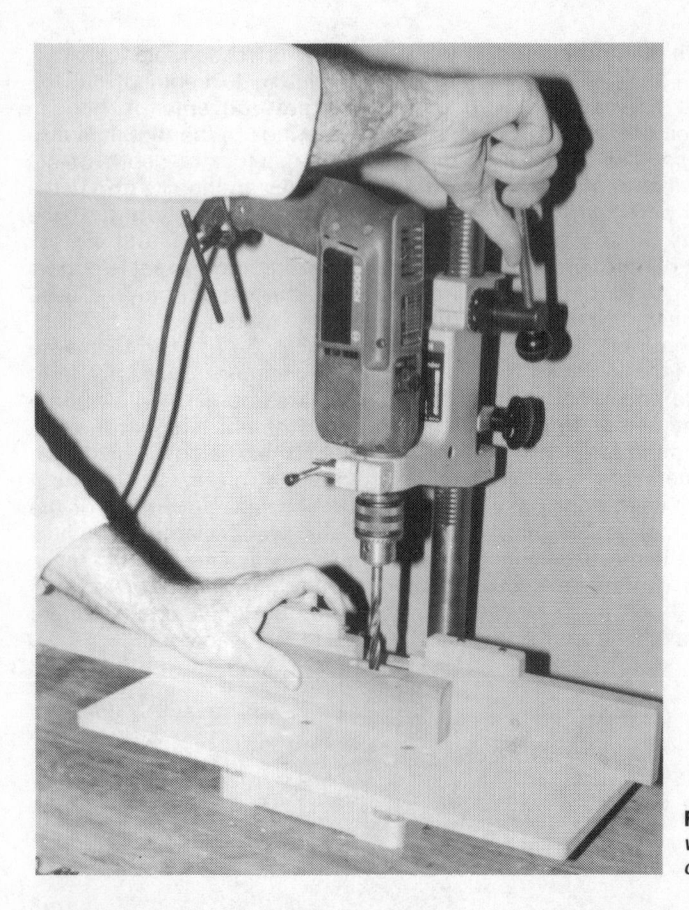

Fig. 73 *Boring out the waste prior to chiselling.*

Mortising with Power Drills and Drill Stands

A power drill can of course be used on its own to bore out the waste from the mortise, prior to using a chisel, and simply as an alternative to a traditional brace. However, it is much more advantageous to use a drill in a drill stand – the boring is vertical, its depth can be governed, and the position of the wood can be controlled relative to the bit.

A false table is needed to exploit the advantages of boring the waste from a mortise. Few manufacturers offer these for their stands, but they can be readily made. A piece of plywood forms the base of this, and needs to be around 530 mm × 250 mm × 13 mm (21 in. × 10 in. × ½ in.). This is bored for bolting to the base of the stand, and a fence of solid wood fixed by bolts and wing nuts to slots in the ply. This allows for the fence to be adjusted in its position on the ply table, and its purpose is to align the wood beneath the bit. In use, the wood is hand held to the fence, and a series of holes made along the mortise. As with hand boring, the mortise has to be completed by chiselling.

Refinements can be made to the false table by adding a second fence at the front, so that the workpiece is more fully controlled as it is moved between the two, and an upper restraint added. The latter would prevent the possibility of the wood lifting as the bit is raised, but this is never more than a slight tendency.

My workshop has an engineer's bench drill in it, for which a mortising table was made years ago. It incorporates a vice to grip the wood, fine adjustment forwards and backwards, and a lever to move the table and wood laterally. Although only a bit is used to remove the waste, the full control given to the wood allows for the holes to be bored so as to overlap, and thus minimal attention is required from the chisel to complete the mortise. It would be possible to devise a similar table for a drill stand of the heavy duty type.

Fig. 74 *Home made mortising table on engineer's drill.*

Further Variations of the Joint

Tenons often have to be formed on the ends of rails which are curved on their edge, and this causes complications where the curve is fairly sharp where it ends at the shoulder of the joint. Where the curve is of a fairly gentle arc, the joint can be cut as normal. It is where the curve is tapering away across the grain that there is weakness with some splitting, and this is difficult to avoid unless the joint is adapted. It is a problem wherever a narrow piece of wood has the grain running crossways, and is known as 'short grain'. The usual way of overcoming this difficulty is to cut away the wood at the edge of the stile, to the depth of the rebate or even a little more – the presence of the rebate makes little difference. The cut is made to show a mitre on the inner corner, and the end of the shoulder likewise cut 45 degrees to match. There is still a risk of the wood splitting at the end of the curve, but the likelihood of this happening is very much reduced.

Frames, and especially door frames, are very likely to have the front inner edges moulded. Where this is formed from end to end, the joint will need modifying on the side adjoining the moulding. The moulding alongside the mortise will need to be cut away to form a flat surface, with the moulding itself cut as a mitre on both members. An alternative way of ensuring the moulding meets properly at the corners, is to form a scribed shoulder. When formed by machine, the scribe is cut across the full width of the shoulder and therefore the mortised member does not require any adjustment. When cut by hand, the scribing is made only part way across the shoulder and the moulding alongside the mortise cut away to match. The scribing is formed by first cutting a mitre at the edge of the shoulder, using

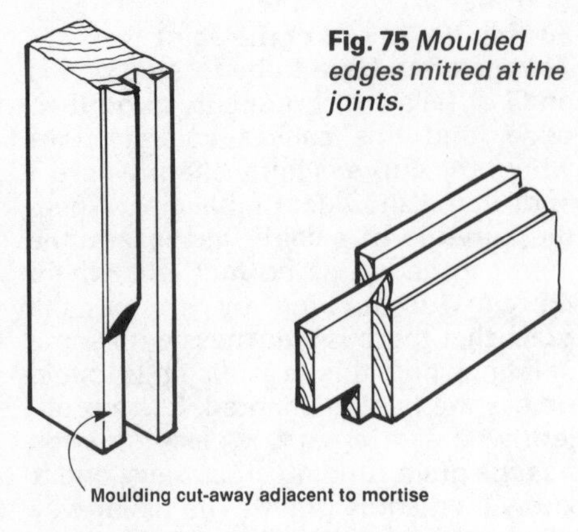

Fig. 75 *Moulded edges mitred at the joints.*

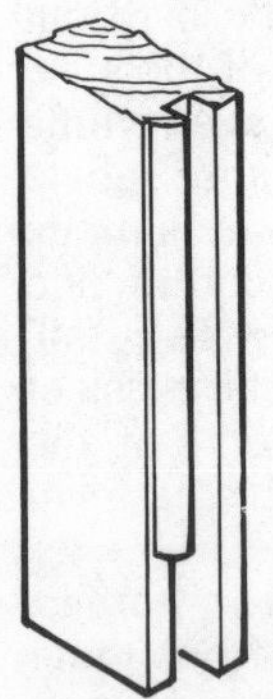

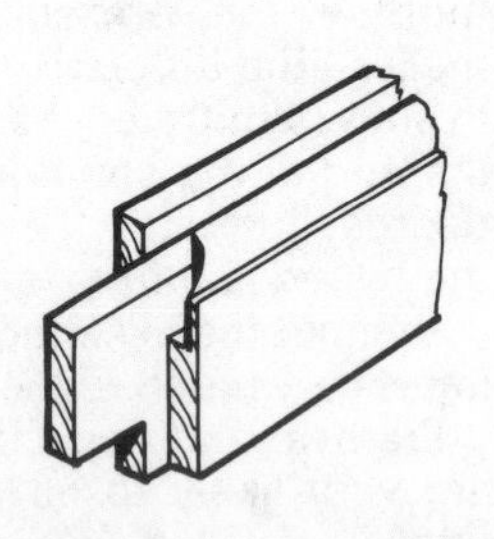

Fig. 76 *Hand-scribed shoulder.*

a chisel and mitre template. The scribe cut is then made with a scribing gouge, for a curved moulding, and is made to the outline shown by the mitre. The appearance of a scribed joint is almost identical to a fully mitred joint, once assembled.

With the router growing in popularity, there is a trend to mould the inner edges of the frame after assembling. This enables a simpler version of the mortise and tenon to be used between the various members, and results in the moulding being radiused in the corners, rather than showing a mitre. Frames carrying panels which are to be moulded in this way need to be tackled while temporarily cramped together without the panels, as these will prevent the router from operating.

Doors are frequently made with the lower part panelled, and the top glazed. Following traditional methods of construction, the glass is fitted into rebates, and the panels into grooves. This arrangement will affect the joints on the rail between upper and lower parts, and requires a tenon with a square shoulder on one side, and a splayed shoulder on the other side. This matches the sloping cut made alongside the mortise, from the edge down to the rebate.

As an alternative to the bridle joint suggested earlier, where a wide member joints into a narrower one, such as the leg of a table into the upper rail, a modified mortise and tenon can be used. The tenon is combined with a trench, and the joint allows scope for simple decorative treatment to the top front of the leg.

Fig. 77 *The mitre template in use.*

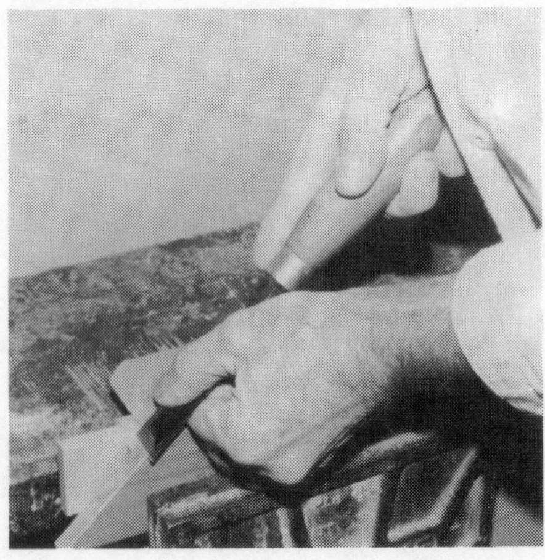

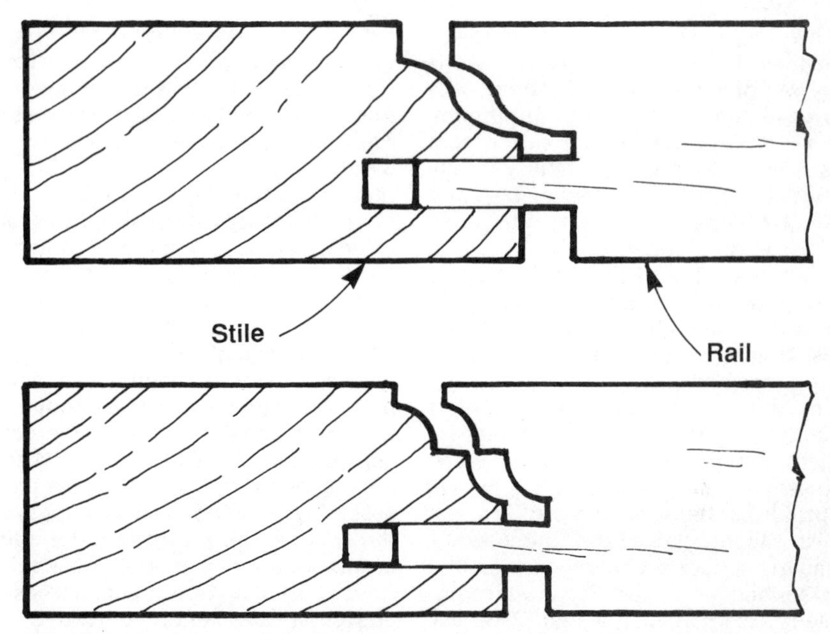

Fig. 78 *Typical joints produced entirely by profile/scriber router cutter sets.*

So far all the joints discussed are for joints which meet at right angles. Most of these can be adapated when the angle between the components is other than 90 degrees, with a sliding bevel being used to mark the shoulder of the tenon. The mortise can be formed with either both ends perpendicular to the surface, or one end perpendicular and the other sloping to match the angle at which the parts meet. The tenon is then made to suit, either one or both edges square to the shoulder. Mortises are not made with one end undercut to match the angle of the tenoned component. Apart from the difficulty of making such a mortise, it is very difficult to assemble the joint when part of a framework.

Because splayed assemblies present problems of cramping, angled joints are often secured by draw-boring. This is explained a little later. This joint is usually used between the strings and newel posts of a staircase, and because of the width of the strings, double tenons are employed with a peg through each one. Angled tenons are normally made as stopped joints.

Where moderate quantities of panelled doors are required, especially the type used for built-in furniture such as kitchen units, a modified form of mortise and tenon might be considered. In fact with this type, there is no mortise as such, as the groove is made deeper than usual, and the short tenon, little more than a tongue, engages with this. Because of the emphasis on the moulded front edge, the groove is made well off-centre, and indeed a lot of the strength of the joint lies in the exact fit which must be attained between the scribed shoulder and the moulded edge.

This joint can only be formed by mechanical means, and the router is one way of achieving this. Indeed, it is the development of router equipment, along with the appropriate cutters that has made this possible. It is virtually impossible to form this joint by hand methods, as the scribed shoulder, over the full width of the rails, simply cannot be made with sufficient accuracy to make a perfect fit over the moulding. For a successful joint, the two parts must fit in a precise way – there is no latitude for inaccuracy.

For the forming of this joint, it is essential to use cutters intended for exactly this purpose. For router work, two sets of cutters are required, known as profile/scriber sets. The profile cutter forms the moulding and the groove, while the scriber set cuts the tenon and the scribed shoulder. A good router table is essential for this work. The use of a totally reliable adhesive is also essential when assembling these doors, and the continued improvement in the quality of adhesives is one reason for the increasing use of this variation of the mortise and tenon.

Securing the Mortise and Tenon

The majority of assembly work is carried out using adhesives, but can be additionally secured in a number of ways. In some cases the joint is locked together without using glue, so that the components can be dismantled later, if required.

One of the commonest ways of securing the through tenon is by wedging. For joinery type work, it is normal to drive the wedges alongside the edges of the tenon, but the cabinet-maker has always preferred to make a couple of saw kerfs near the edges of the tenon, then drive the wedges into these. With either of these methods, the mortises have to be prepared by creating space for the wedges, known as 'wedge room'. The outer part of the mortise is made rather wider by tapering the ends. The amount of slope is usually between 3 mm – 6 mm (⅛ in.–¼ in.) approximately, depending on the size of the joint. The taper must extend to around three quarters of the way down the mortise, to ensure the tightening effect of the wedges is effective, well down towards the shoulder of the joint.

'Fox wedging' is a technique employed for stopped joints. The tenon is prepared with saw kerfs as above, and the ends of the mortise undercut by approximately 5 – 10 degrees. Wedges are inserted into the kerfs at the time of assembly. When pressure is applied by the cramps, the wedges hit the bottom of the mortise and are consequently driven up the kerfs. This forces the edges of the tenon outwards, and spreads them to fill the whole of the mortise. Considerable judgement and care are needed for successful fox wedging, as everything has to be just right for the joint to be tight, without a gap at the shoulder. What has to be kept in mind with this technique is that once the joint is even partly assembled then you are committed, as it is usually impossible to take apart and start again. All wedges should have a slope close to 1:7, and are glued as driven in.

A very strong method of securing the joint is by 'pegging'. This method can be used on both through and stopped joints, and in the case of the former is usually in addition to wedging. If a round peg is used, it is usually a piece of dowel pointed at one end and with its diameter in proportion to the size of the joint. In use, a hole is bored to pass through the assembled joint, and the peg driven home. The hole should be bored somewhat nearer the shoulder,

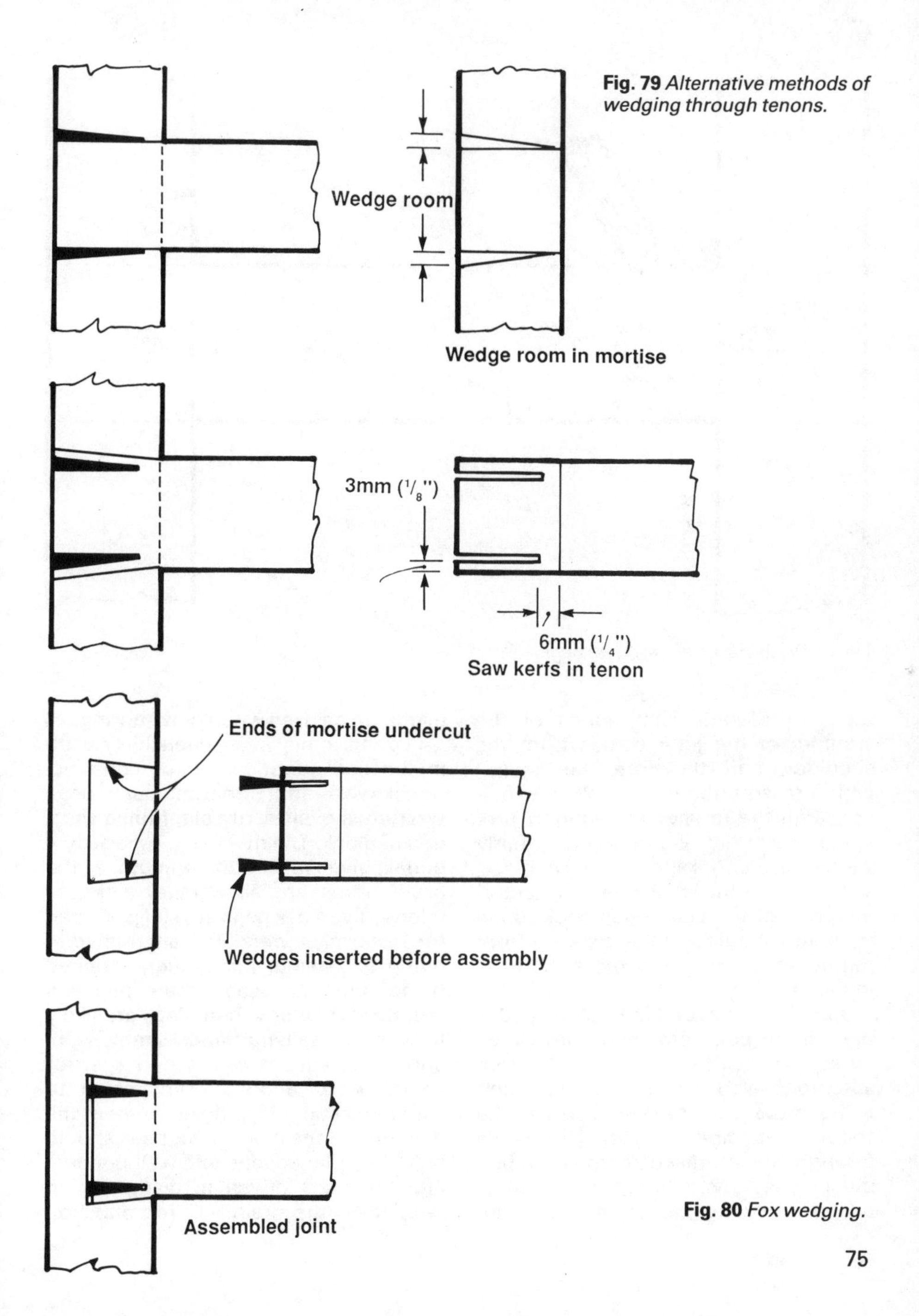

Fig. 79 *Alternative methods of wedging through tenons.*

Fig. 80 *Fox wedging.*

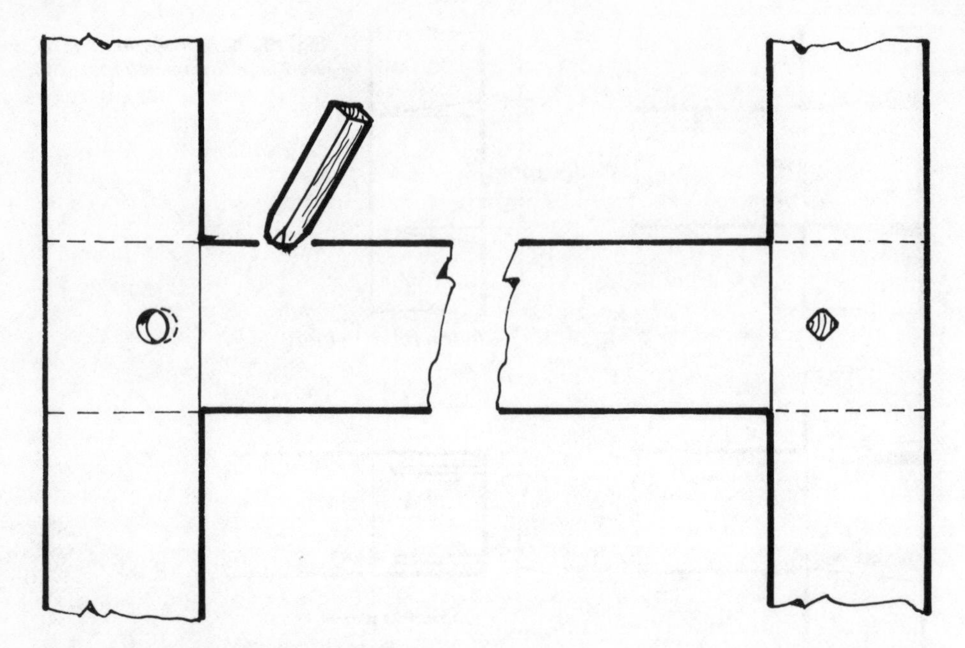

Fig. 81 *Draw-boring with square pegs.*

for two reasons. First, much of the strength of the joint comes from the shoulder, and therefore the nearer, within reason, the peg is to the shoulder, then the greater the support provided. Secondly, if the wood is fairly wide, then shrinkage can take place, and as the joint is, in effect, locked at the point of the peg, a gap could open up at the shoulder if the distance from peg to shoulder is any more than the minimum.

A double variation of the dowel peg is the square peg combined with draw-boring. The holes are prepared before assembly, with the one in the tenon being made 1.5 mm (1⁄16 in.) nearer the shoulder compared with the hole through the mortised member. When the peg is driven home, the joint is pulled tightly together. A dowel peg can of course be used when draw-boring.

Pegged joints were extensively used in the past, both for heavy constructional work and furniture. Early pegs were always riven, or split, from a short end of plank. The riven peg, especially if of oak, gives maximum strength, as the grain fibres are all parallel with the edges. Riven oak pegs are still preferred for restoration work. The alternative to riving is sawing, but straight grained wood must be used or the peg will crumble when driven in. Pegs are likely to be between 6 mm and 13 mm (¼ in. and ½ in.) square, or maybe larger for heavy work, and the pegs sawn to square section slightly less than the diameter of the hole. The arrises should be lightly planed, one end well pointed, and the pegs driven in diagonally in relation to the grain. On reproduction and restoration work, the pegs are sometimes left to protrude slightly, and carefully chiselled so as to combine function with a little decoration.

Screws provide a simple means of securing a joint, especially stopped joints, as an alternative to fox wedging. This method is only used where the screws are not seen, for example, the leg to a small table. For maximum benefit, the screws should penetrate as close to the outer surface as possible, and are always best if staggered in relation to the grain.

A nail or panel pin can be used in a similar way to a screw, especially if the mortise is in a thicker piece of wood than the tenoned member. A pin is less strong than a screw, but is a useful method to adopt if cramps are in short supply. Pinning the joints enables the cramps to be removed before the glue has dried, and driving the pins in after cramping will hold the joint tight when the pressure is slackened off.

Another way of securing the joint is a variation of the tusk tenon. The tenon is made to penetrate the mortise by a considerable amount, and a mortise is cut in the actual tenon. This allows a wedge to be driven in, which draws the joint tightly together and holds it firm. The mortise must be slightly overcut at its inner end to ensure the wedge will tighten effectively. This method must be accepted as a feature of the design, lending itself to simple, robust constructions.

A method of securing the joint, much used on commercially produced joinery work, is by 'star' dowel pins. These are made of a non-rusting alloy, are star shaped in section, and pointed at one end with a 'barbed' feature. Different sizes are available, and are driven through the joint similarly to an ordinary dowel.

CHAPTER 7

BOX AND CORNER JOINTS

Box or corner joints are used where the components meet when on edge, rather than flatways. In woodworking terms, box construction does not just apply to boxes, but when an item is made essentially in the form of a box, and where the wood is usually relatively wide but fairly thin.

In this chapter we look at alternatives to dovetailing, dowelling, and biscuit jointing. Most of the remaining corner joints are formed directly at the ends of the wood, therefore it is essential that the material is carefully prepared to length, with the ends dead square. A hand sawn end is not usually sufficiently accurate, and if not cut by a circular saw, the ends must be shot by plane.

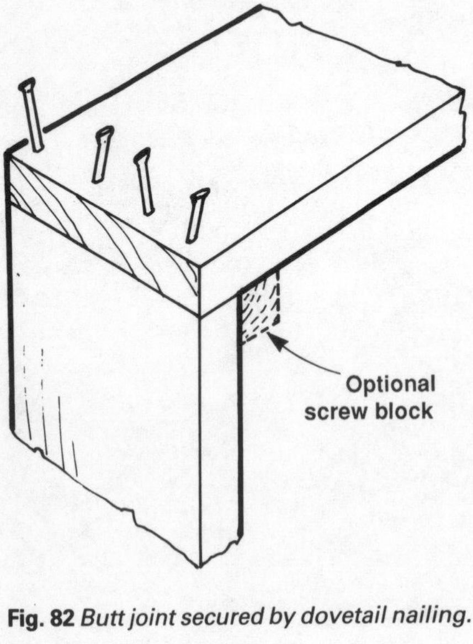

Fig. 82 *Butt joint secured by dovetail nailing.*

BUTT JOINT

The simplest corner joint is the butt, only likely to be used for basic constructions. Adhesive is of negligible value for such a joint because one of the surfaces in contact is wholly end grain, and adhesive has poor strength on end grain. This means the joint relies almost entirely on either nails, or screws. Nails are most effective when driven in at a slight angle. This is known as 'dovetail nailing'. Not only do nails driven in in this way have a locking effect, they grip better because of going at least partly across the grain.

This joint can be made stronger by a 'screw block' on the inner corner. These blocks are usually around 20 mm (¾ in.) square, and are bored so that screws can be driven into both components. Ideally, the holes in these blocks should be slots, especially if the components are wide, as the slots will allow for 'movement' which can take place across the grain. An alternative to screw blocks is glue blocks, which are also around 20 mm (¾ in.) square but are best glued in place in short lengths, around 50–63 mm (2 in.–2½ in.). These bed in place better, and also allow for some movement if spaces are left between them.

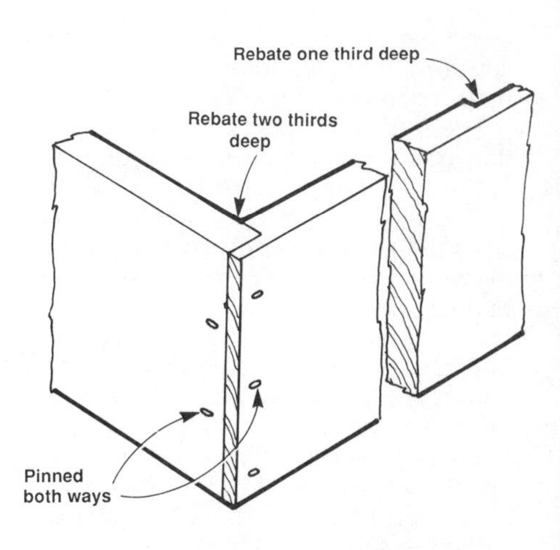

Fig. 83 *Rebated and pinned.*

REBATED CORNER JOINT

One piece is rebated to allow the other to fit into this, and while there is no interlocking of the components, this joint is far more satisfactory than the plain butt because of the better location offered by the rebate. The depth of the rebate for this joint can vary from one third the thickness of the wood, to two thirds or even more, and the deeper the rebate the less end grain is visible. If the end grain is rounded over on completion, there is little obvious evidence of the joint. A fairly deep rebate also allows for pins to be driven in from

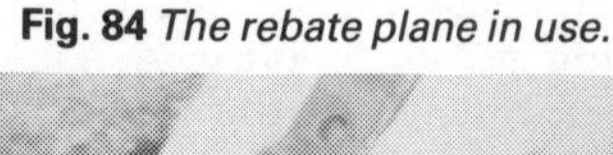

Fig. 84 *The rebate plane in use.*

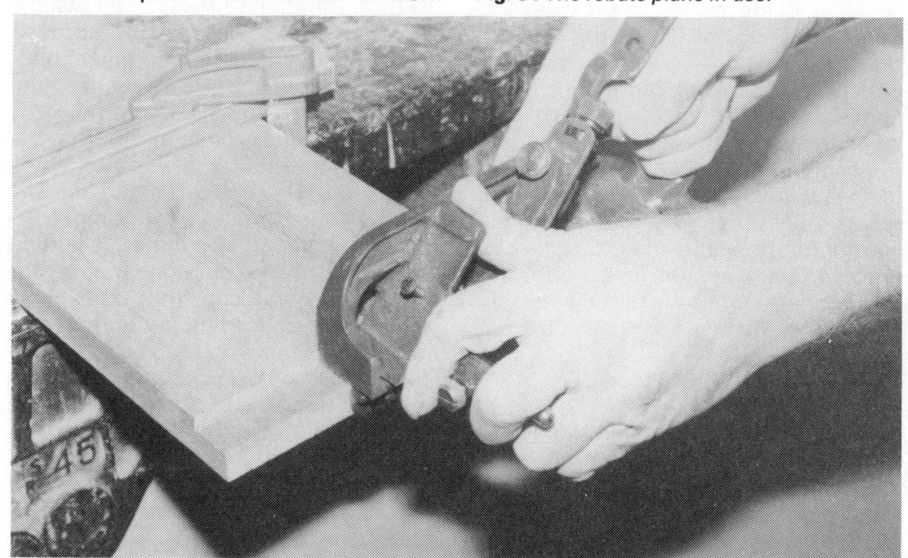

adjoining sides, and because the pins are at right angles to one another, they have a good locking effect.

The rebate is marked out with a cutting gauge because of its cross grain nature. To form entirely by hand, the cut across the grain is made first by saw, then the waste is chiselled away by working from the end. A shoulder, bullnose or similar plane is then used for the final trimming down to the line. The rebate can be completely formed with a rebate plane fitted with a guide, fence and spur, this plane also being known as a sash fillister. A rebating attachment in a power drill can also be used. Forming the rebate by power is similar to forming a corner halving, the cuts essentially the same but the proportions different. It can be cut by radial arm saw, or by router used either in a table, or hand held, as for rebating along the grain. It is certain that more than one pass will be needed. If the wood is narrow, the cut made on the router table must be formed using the crosscut guide so as to provide adequate support, but where the wood is reasonably wide, it can be controlled directly by the long fence. The same applies to using the sawbench, and when the rip fence is used this requires re-positioning for each pass made. The bandsaw is not suitable for cutting the rebate unless the wood is quite narrow, and therefore stable when on its edge. A power plane cannot be used for cutting a rebate across the grain unless the limit of the rebate is first cut by saw.

THE TONGUED CORNER JOINT

This has much better mechanical strength than the rebated joint, but results in a lot of end grain showing. The proportions of the joint need careful choosing to arrive at the best balance. The wood between the groove and the end is an area of short grain, somewhat weak, and could split away under unfavourable conditions. When the two pieces are of equal thickness, the tongue should be around one third the thickness, and its projection the same.

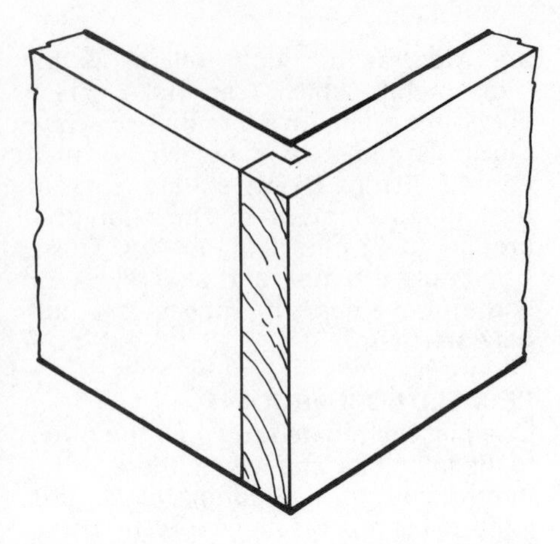

Fig. 85 *Tongued joint.*

Cutting the joint by hand follows the procedures just described for forming the rebate to create the tongue, and for cutting the trenches. However, the joint is particularly suitable for forming by power tool or machine, and both parts can be formed with the router when hand held. The trench should first be formed when routing, and made to match a standard size cutter. It is then easier to form the tongue to match this, rather than working the other way round. Invariably when jointing, two or more similar joints have to be cut, and it is important where re-setting of tools is required, that all cuts at the one setting are carried out before adjusting the equipment and proceeding. This ensures consistency of cutting, helps to gain and maintain accuracy, and usually means time saved.

THE TONGUED AND LAPPED JOINT

This is a rather more sophisticated version of the tongued joint. As well as increasing the gluing area, the amount of endgrain which is visible on completion is much less than with the tongued joint. While it is not impossible to form the joint entirely by hand, it is not recommended, although it can be cut with a rebating attachment. Again, the router is probably the best means of forming this joint, but considerable care is needed to ensure a proper fit without gaps; the joint must be tight to be effective.

MITRED AND TONGUED

For the tongued mitre, the mitres themselves must be first prepared. This can be carried out on the radial arm saw by tilting the headstock, or on a saw bench providing the table, or the saw arbor, will tilt up to 45 degrees. Alternatively, the mitre can first be sawn by hand, then trimmed by plane in a mitre shooting box. These cannot be bought and therefore have to be made in the workshop. For most methods of forming the groove, a piece of scrap wood is needed, with one edge mitred. The mitre on the scrap then forms a flat surface, against which the tool forming the groove can abut and be guided.

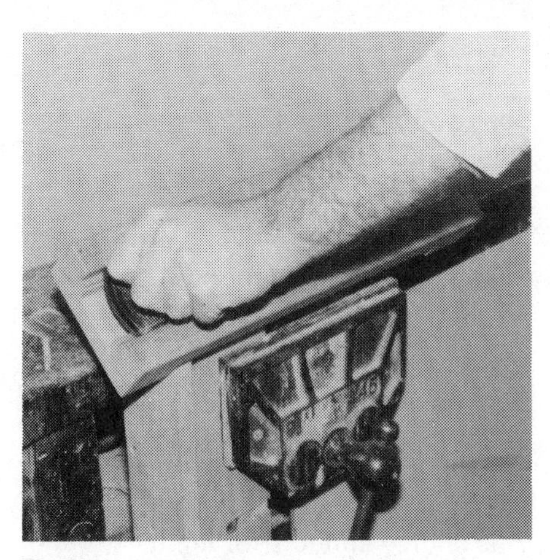

Fig. 86 *Using the mitre shooting board.*

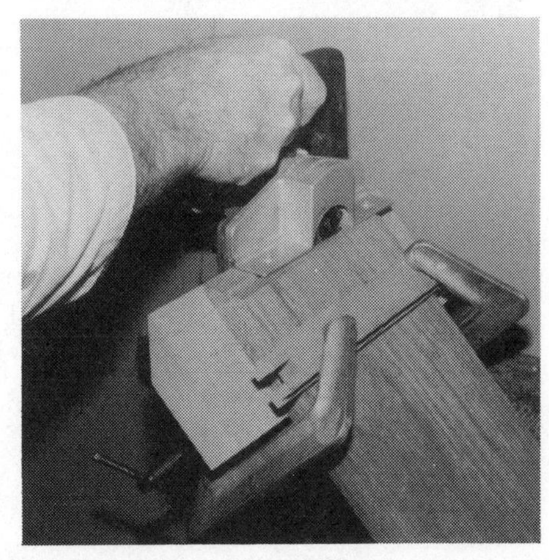

Fig. 87 *Grooving with a milling cutter.*

The power drill with a rebating or milling attachment is one way of forming the groove, using either a grooving cutter or the small circular saw blade. The ever-adaptable router provides an easy way of cutting the grooves. A biscuit jointer can also be used; the highly efficient circular saw blade on this tool provides a useful means of cutting many types of grooves, providing their size and position are within the limitations of the tool. Here it is being used simply to form a groove, not a biscuit joint. It is possible to form the groove on the radial arm saw, with the headstock set at 45 degrees as for the mitre. The circular saw bench, though, does not lend itself to forming this cut. Note that the tongue is better if

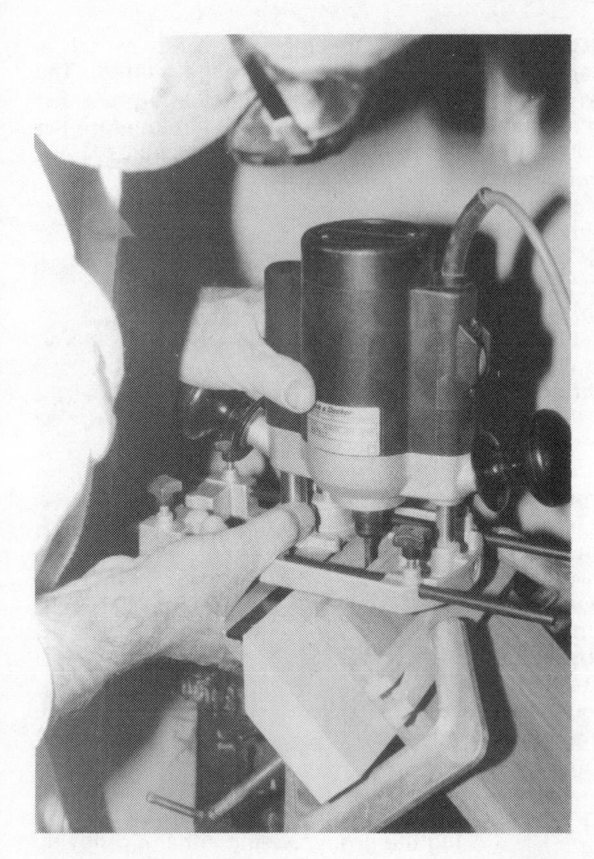

Fig. 88 *The router in use hand held.*

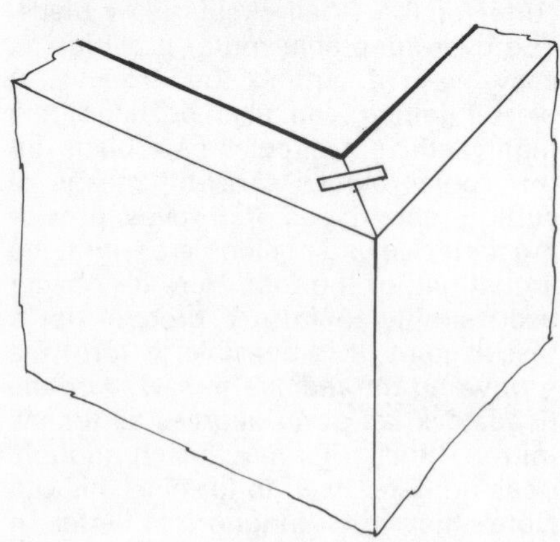

Fig. 89 *Mitred and tongued.*

positioned nearer to the inner corner, enabling the groove to be made reasonably deep without unduly weakening the wood.

Maximum strength is gained from the tongue if it is cut so that the grain runs crossways. As well as providing good strength, tongues cut this way will be barely visible on the edges of the assembled parts, as the grain on the surfaces will be in the same direction.

MITRED AND FEATHERED

This is only suitable for lighter types of constructions, where strength is not a prime consideration, for instance trinket boxes and sliding trays within drawers. It is both attractive and intriguing if the veneer feathers are of a wood of contrasting colour.

Fig. 90 *Feathered mitre joint.*

Exact mitres are formed at the ends of the components, then glued together. Blocks with rebates in them should be made so as to fit around the corners, and pressure applied from a webbing cramp, or even string. The work must be left to dry before proceeding.

It is wise to try a sample saw cut in a piece of scrap, and check that the veneer gives a reasonably tight fit. Veneer thicknesses vary, as do saw kerfs, and a good fit is desirable. The position of the saw cuts should be first marked out so that they are neatly spaced at matching angles, and all of the same depth. Splaying the saw kerfs gives a dovetailing effect, and so adds to the locking benefit of the feathers. Glue must be worked well into the saw kerfs, and the feathers inserted a little oversize. Carefully level by chisel and fine planing, after the adhesive has thoroughly dried out. Apart from the initial mitres, this is a joint which can only be made by hand methods.

COMB JOINT

Also known as the finger joint, this provides good mechanical strength and has a considerable gluing area. The joint looks best when the total number of fingers is an odd number, as this gives full symmetry with the edges of the joint matching. The joint looks even better when the width of the fingers does not exceed the thickness of the wood and, the more fingers there are, within reason, the stronger the joint.

This joint has increased in popularity in recent years, largely because of the combing jig attachments which can be used with many circular saw benches, and combing/dovetailing jigs, which can be used with power drills fitted with the special cutter required.

The joint can be quickly and easily formed by hand, and is more straightforward than dovetailing. The extent of the joint from the end of the wood is marked with a cutting gauge, or alternatively, a try square and marking knife. It can be an advantage to make this line slightly in excess of the thickness of the wood, so that the fingers when cut and fitted together will pro-

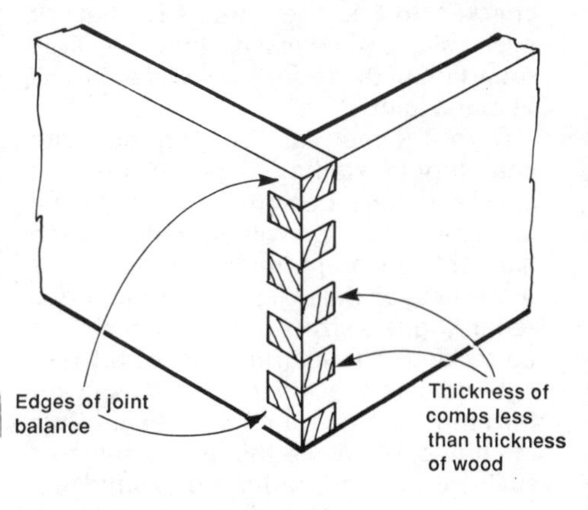

Fig. 91 *Comb or finger joint.*

trude by about 1 mm (3/64 in.). Levelling off and smoothing then take place after gluing up.

The lines which indicate the width of the fingers are best marked with a mortise gauge, advancing the stock of the gauge until the marking out is completed. Shading the waste is particularly important with this joint, not simply to ensure the correct parts are removed but to be certain that the sawing is on the waste side of the many lines.

Cutting the joint is started by sawing down the grain with a back saw. In most cases this can be carried out by simply sawing straight down, working from one side. In the fairly rare cases of this joint being used on material over around 20 mm (3/4 in.) thick, they are best cut by sawing from both sides in a similar way to cutting the cheeks of tenons.

The bulk of the waste is now removed with a coping saw. As this saw cannot be used with any real accuracy, the cutting should be a little away from the line. Trimming down to the line is carried out by chisel, with the cutting taking place part way from both sides. These chiselled surfaces must be checked to see they are quite flat, or even slightly concave. Even a little rounding of these surfaces will spoil the fit of the joint.

Comb joints can be formed with combing/dovetailing jigs, using the special cutters designed to match the jig. One of my jigs will only allow for a 'lapped' version of the finger joint to be made, and all these jigs have limitations regarding the sizes of wood which can be tackled. The instructions with these jigs indicate that they can be used for forming both comb and dovetail joints in chipboard. While this is strictly true, such joints in chipboard would be unsatisfactory. Chipboard, when cut into small parts, as required for both these joints, is very weak, and therefore projecting parts are extremely likely to crumble and break away. In addition, chipboard is very abrasive, and requires T.C.T. cutters for it to be worked satisfactorily. The cutters provided with the jigs are not tipped, and therefore would become very blunt after cutting a very small number of joints in chipboard. Both these joints can be formed with success in good quality plywood, which is much stronger than chipboard and does not crumble in the same way. Even so, plywood blunts cutting edges faster than does solid wood, and therefore tipped cutters should be employed when power tools are being used in conjunction with ply. Apart from the above observations, the instructions relating to the jig must be carefully followed.

The combing jig for use with a circular sawbench must match the machine, because the sliding bar of the jig has to fit exactly in the cross cut groove of the table. In addition, the distance from this to the blade must correspond. However, there is a way around the above requirements. I once found myself the owner of a combing jig which did not match my small sawbench, and I solved the problem as follows: a false table of 13 mm (1/2 in.) ply was made to fit the top of the sawbench, and secured by four machine screws inserted into holes drilled and tapped into this. A groove was also formed in the ply, to match the bar of the jig in both size and distance from the blade. This false table can be readily removed for normal use of the machine.

A wobble saw arbor, or washers, is also essential for box combing. These allow the blade to oscillate as it rotates, and are adjustable giving a much wider cut than the normal kerf. The maximum

Fig. 92 *The combing jig in use.*

width of cut that can be made is usually around 16 mm (5/8 in.), so the washers are adjusted to equal the width of the fingers, which of course is the same as the waste removed at each pass of the wood. The height of the blade above the table is set to equal the extent of the joint, which is the same as the thickness of the wood, or very slightly more to allow for subsequent levelling.

Jigs vary slightly in their design and operation, so again specific instructions must be carefully followed. When you are using the combing jig, a trial cut should be made prior to tackling the actual work, but it is essential for such trials to be made in wood of exactly the same width and thickness as the work-pieces. Sequence of working is important, and face marks strictly observed and followed. Once set, these jigs can carry out all the cutting of the joints for a box in a few minutes.

The size of wood which can be tackled with these jigs is limited in its length, because the material has to be hand-held and supported as it passes the blade. The actual length which can be safely held and controlled on its end depends on its weight, and also the size of the vertical fence of the jig, against which it has to be held.

CHAPTER 8

DOVETAIL JOINTS

Dovetails, like all other joints, can be made in many variations, and are often considered to be the most difficult to make. This is not so if the approach is correct – accurate marking out followed by careful and precise cutting. It is also necessary, however, to have an understanding of the joint and its various forms, and the proportions to adopt. Good tool control combined with a certain amount of knack are essential to produce joints which are a good fit and therefore both strong and neat.

The joint does quite literally derive its name from the tail of the dove. This bird's tail is fan shaped with the edges splayed outwards, and it is the non-parallel edges which make the dovetail joint quite different from all others. The joint is much associated with box-type constructions, but it has other applications. The slope creates the locking effect, which means that the components can only be assembled, and therefore the parts withdrawn, in one direction. This needs to be remembered while deciding on the layout of the joint, in order to maximise the strength characteristics of the dovetails.

The slope or angle of the joint is very important, and must neither be too steep nor too flat. If too flat, the locking effect is largely lost, and if excessively steep the joint will lack strength. The latter creates areas of 'short grain', a factor mentioned earlier, making it weak and prone to splitting. The slopes of 1:8 is preferred for hardwoods, and 1:6 for softwoods, because some compression takes place on assembly. This compression is dependent on both the slope adopted and the fit of the joint, but the denser the wood the less the fibres of the grain are likely to compress. In practice, many craftsmen, including myself, adopt a slope of 1:7 for all timbers, unless there is a special reason to vary it.

Note that it is usual to have the parts called the pins at the edges of the wood, making marking out easier, and consistent with variations of the joint, such as the lap dovetail, where it is essential to have pins at the edges. It is also customary to have the joint arranged so that the slope is positioned to gain most strength from its locking effect. Thus for a wall mounted cabinet, for instance, the pins would be positioned on the horizontal members to give maximum strength, and this applies whatever variation of the joint is used.

THE COMMON DOVETAIL

The common or box dovetail is a 'through' joint, that is, it is fully exposed

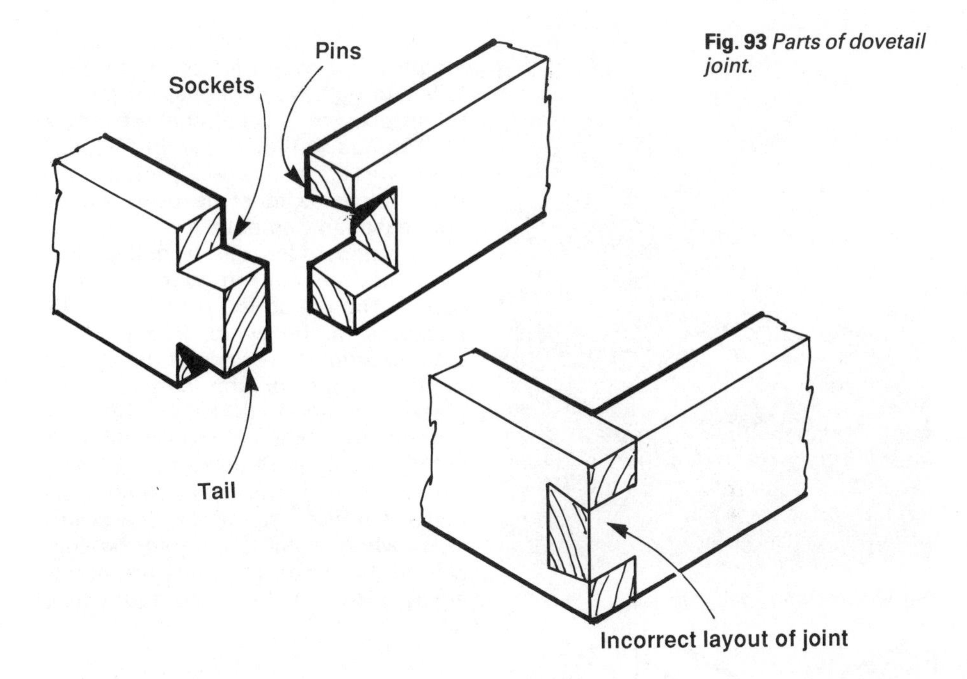

Fig. 93 *Parts of dovetail joint.*

on both surfaces. For most applications, the pins are made a little smaller than the tails, but too few pins with large tails do not give the best layout. Where the joints are to be seen and therefore appearance is important, the pins are often made quite slender to give a neat and delicate joint. There is, however, a reduction in strength when the pins are made very thin, and this must be kept in mind when marking out the joint. Slender pins are often seen in old furniture, but are only suitable where minimal strength is required of the joint, for example, small boxes and drawer construction.

Where strength is of prime consideration, the pins and tails are made to approximately the same size. The strength of the joint is largely dependent on the ratio of wood removed, to wood retained.

When I am forming dovetails, I always cut and trim the wood to the finished length required, without any allowance on the length for levelling the outer surfaces of the joint on com-

Fig. 94 *The common or box dovetail.*

pletion. While a slight excess on the length of the wood for common dovetails can be advantageous, for lap and other forms of dovetail, the wood must be trimmed to the final length needed, therefore I adopt this policy for all dovetails. The ends must be dead square, and reasonably smooth.

The extent of the joint from the end of the wood is marked with a cutting gauge. The gauge is set to exactly the thickness of the wood, and the lines gauged around the ends of the components, except for the edges of the pieces, on which the pins are to be formed. The gauge should be used lightly, so that the blade only scores the surface of the wood. Heavy gauging can make it difficult to remove deep incisions when cleaning the joint on completion. Common dovetails are almost always formed between components of

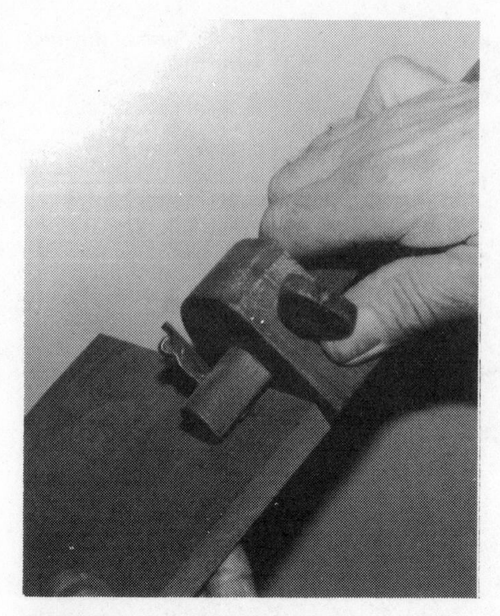

Fig. 95 *The cutting gauge in use.*

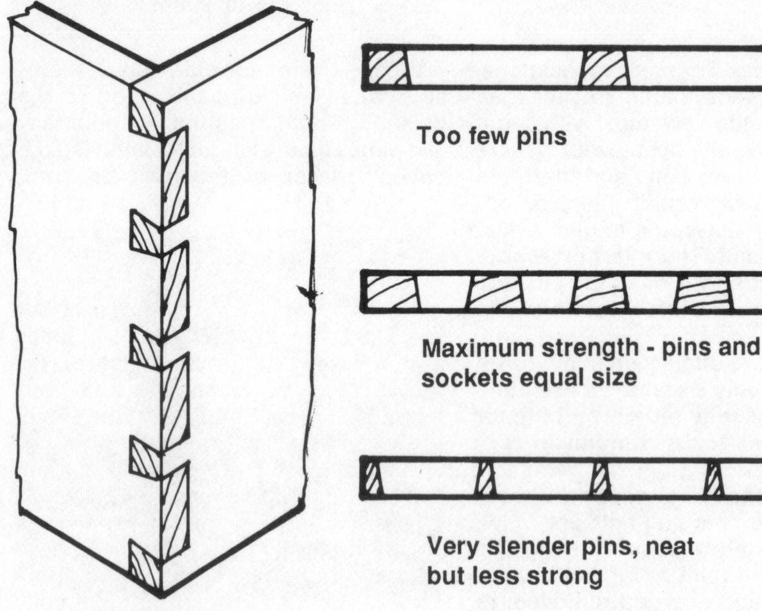

Fig. 96 *Layout of common or box dovetails.*

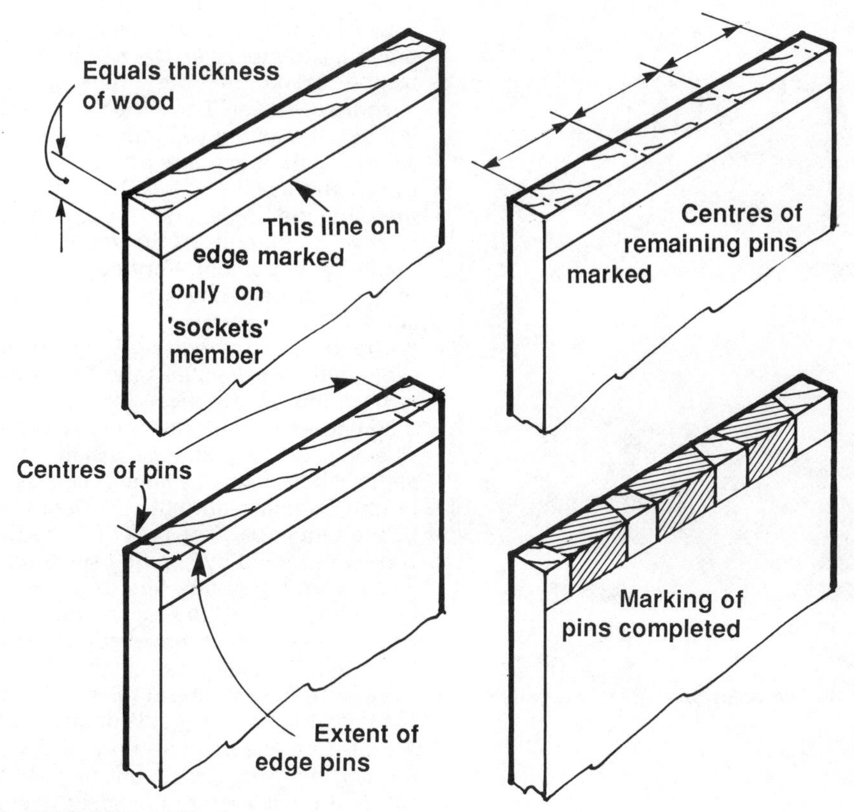

Fig. 97 *Marking out for pins.*

the same thickness. On the rare occasions when this is not so, the gauge lines must allow for this.

Craftsmen have different ways of going about forming dovetail joints; some prefer 'pins first', and others 'tails first'.I believe that by far the greater majority of craftsmen start by cutting the pins first, which is the method I follow, and can be adopted for the rather more advanced variations of the joint. The tails are then marked from the pins, and dovetails are the only joints in woodwork where one part of the joint is marked by directly pencilling around the other, so that the tails are individually matched to suit each set of pins.

Normally, the width of the pins on the inner surface of the wood is made about equal to the thickness of the wood, or possibly slightly less. This dimension is then marked on the end of the wood to indicate the outer pins, and a mark also made to show the centre of each of these two pins. The distance between these centre lines is then divided up, according to the number of pins decided on, and the widths of the intermediate pins marked centrally about these lines.

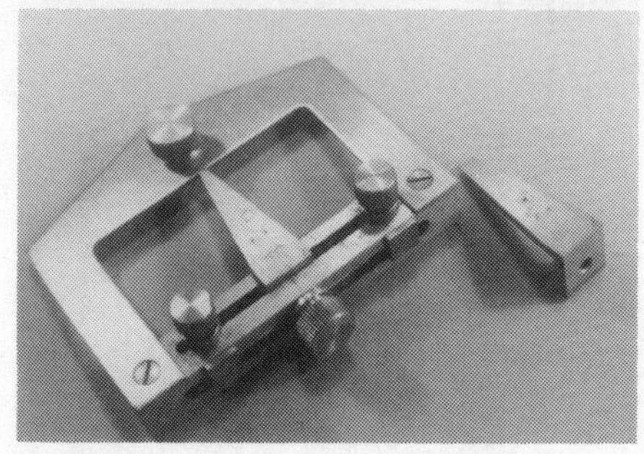

Fig. 98 *(top). Simple types of dovetail templates.*

Fig. 99 *Fully adjustable dovetail template.*

The pins slope on the end of the wood, and these lines can be marked in a variety of ways. A sliding bevel can be set to the required angle and used, a simple template of wood can be quickly made, or using metal or plastic templates with fixed slopes, all popular methods. More sophisticated dovetail templates are also on the market, which allow for either 1:6 or 1:8 slopes to be marked, and can be set so that only the centre line of the pins need be initially indicated. Once the pins are marked, a try square is used to mark the lines on the face of the wood, but there is nothing to be gained from marking the reverse side.

Unless the joints are seen on completion, experience allows for short cuts to be taken on the marking out described earlier. For simplified marking out, the expert will indicate just the centre of the pins, the rest is done by eye at the sawing stage. The width of the pins, the angle, and the square cut relative to the ends of the wood are all made by judgement. Very good uniformity can be gained with practice, especially for 'routine' work.

The start of the cutting is down the grain with the dovetail saw. The wood is held low in the vice, and the kerfs made to touch the line on the waste side. In order to maintain consistency of angle, it helps if all the lines which slope in one direction are cut first, followed by the remainder. The bulk of the waste is now removed by coping saw, a little away from the gauge line to allow for final trimming. This is completed by chisel, preferably bevel-edged and sharpened to a fairly low angle. Choose a reasonably wide chisel relative to the space on the narrower side of the slope. A mallet can be used at this stage, and the chiselling is carried out from both sides. There is a danger of some woods crumbling to an extent in the centre, as it is being chiselled from the second side. With these woods, it is sometimes better to work mainly from one side, dispense with the mallet, and pare the wood away by hand pressure only. The sawn sides of the pins do not require any attention from the chisel.

Because of their individual matching, it is essential that dovetail joints are clearly marked to ensure that the final assembly of the components is as they have been prepared. These marks are best made on the outer surfaces, as the inner ones are normally cleaned up prior to assembly which would remove them. Each set of tails is now marked

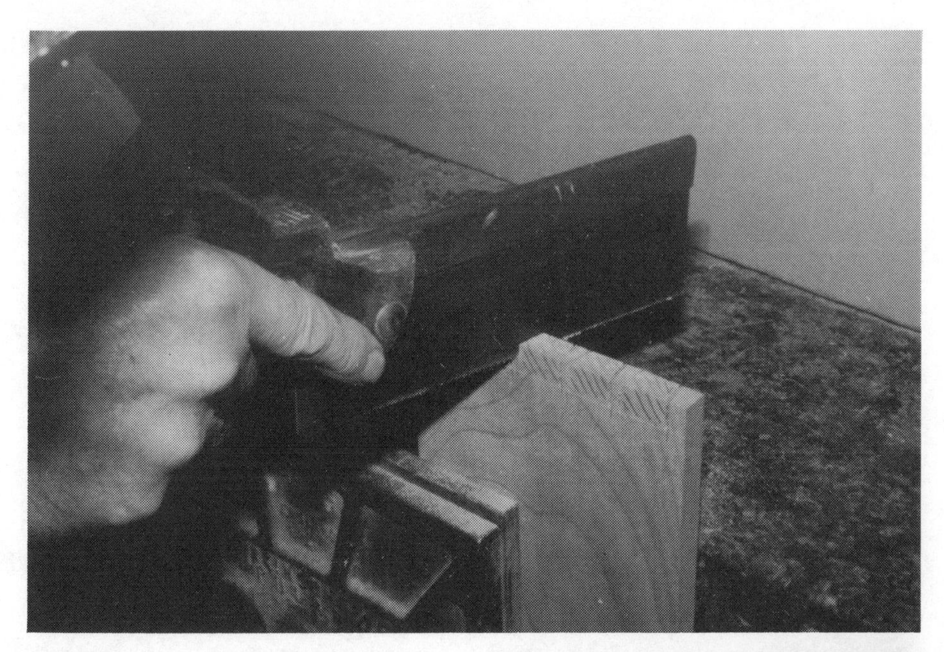

Fig. 100 *(top). Start of cutting the joint.*

Fig. 101 *(right). Trimming down to the gauge line.*

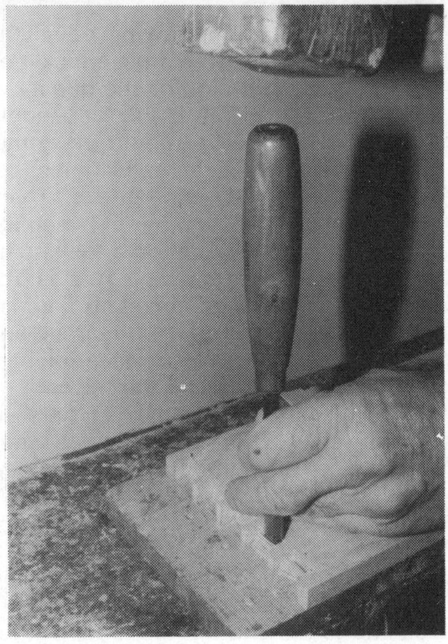

from the corresponding pins. The pencil you use is important – it should be grade H or HH, with a sharp, slender point. It is also essential that the point of the pencil makes its mark immediately alongside the edges of the pins. It is easy to get these all-important pencil lines wrong, but also easy to get them correct if a little care is used. The sloping lines produced can be squared across the ends of the wood as additional guide lines for the saw, again, a stage dispensed with as experience is gained.

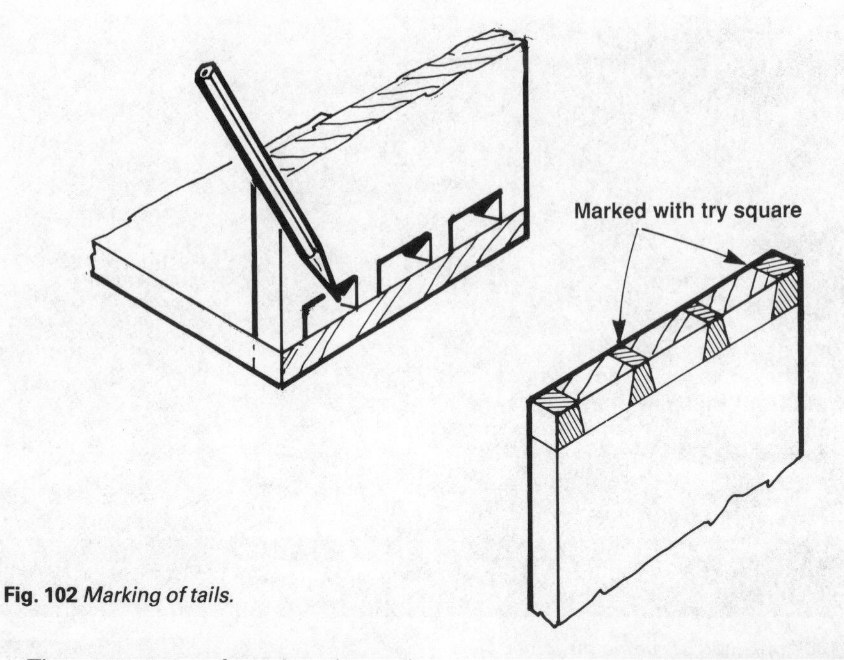

Fig. 102 *Marking of tails.*

The next stage of sawing down the sides of the tails is the most critical one of the whole cutting, for the quality of the fit of the joint is highly dependent on this. The sawing should be immediately adjacent to the pencil lines, but so that they are just left on. There should not be any gap left between the kerf and the line, nor should the line be removed by the sawing. This is the stage in cutting dovetails which requires most care and judgement, and with practice, the sawn surfaces will not need any attention from the chisel.

The waste from the sockets is removed in just the same way as when cutting the pins, that is, by coping saw and chisel. The waste at the outer sockets, however, is removed entirely by dovetail saw. A useful dodge to adopt is to form tiny chamfers on the inner corners of the tails, but these must not extend to the end of the wood, or they

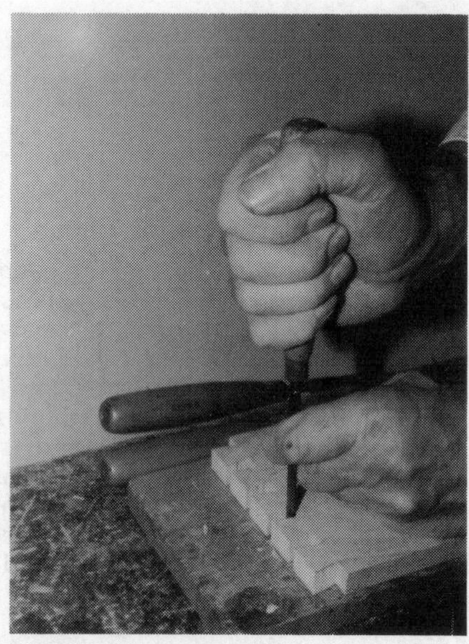

Fig. 103 *Chiselling waste from sockets.*

will be visible on completion of the joint. The chamfers provide a 'lead-in' for the pins, make assembly easier, and prevent the possibility of damage to the corners.

It is a mistake to make trial assemblies of the joint several times before the actual gluing up stage. Each time the joint is assembled the fibres of the surfaces in contact compress a little, and the tight fit essential to a good joint is lost. With experience, you will only have to start the pins in the sockets to ensure that all is well, and a glance will indicate from this partial assembly that the joint will go fully home when pressure is applied. No attempt should be made to give the pins a 'taper' effect, in the belief that this will make the joint tighter as it is driven fully home. There is no need for this, and can result in the wood splitting.

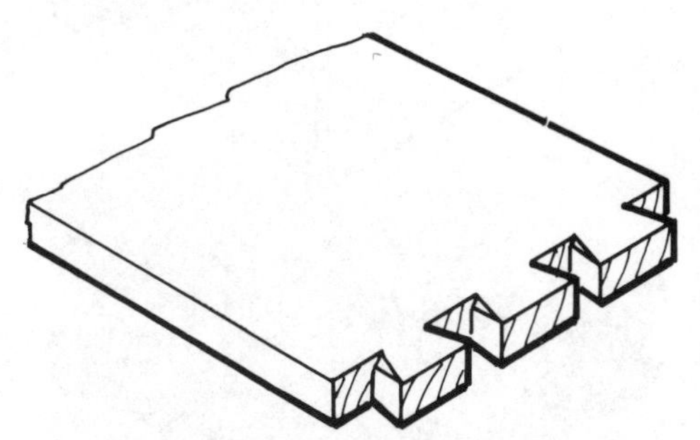

Fig. 104 *Tiny chamfers provide 'lead-in' for pins.*

Modifications to the Common Dovetail
Sometimes it is necessary to show a mitre on one edge of the wood, or indeed even both, and this must be allowed for when the pins are marked out. The extent of the mitre is made about the same as the widest part of the pin, which means, in effect, the outer pin where the mitre is to be formed is made double width.

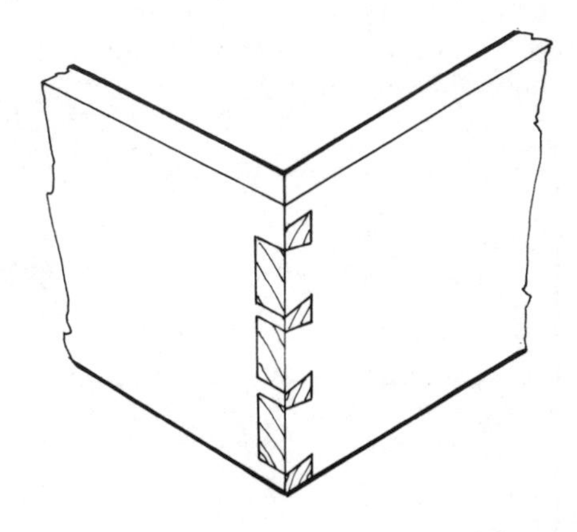

Fig. 105 *Joint modified to show mitre at edge.*

Another modification is where the inner edges of the material being dovetailed are to be rebated. The outer pin has to be adjusted in two ways. It must be made rather wider than the extent of the rebate, and its thickness must be reduced by the depth of the rebate. Exactly the same modification to the outer pin is needed, if the inner surface

Fig. 106 *Joint modified to accommodate rebate.*

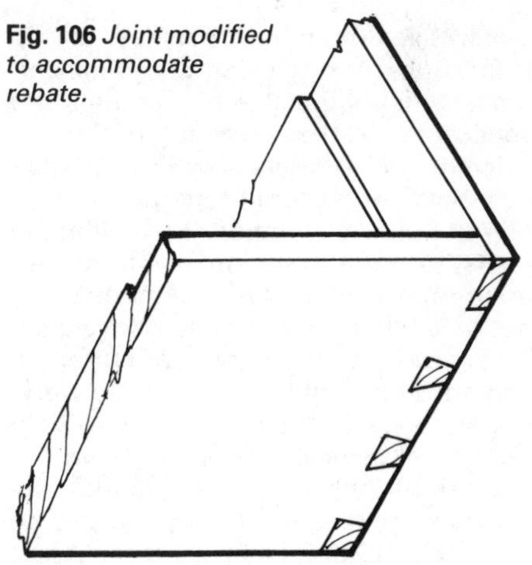

is to be grooved, assuming the groove is fairly close to the edge.

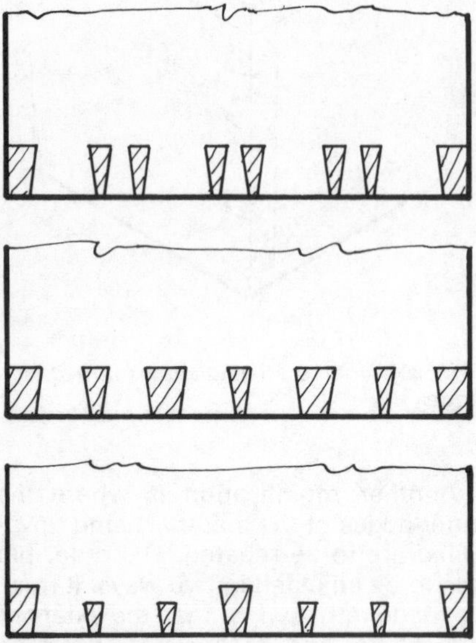

Fig. 107 *Decorative dovetails.*

Decorative Common Dovetails

In furniture making generally, joints and other constructional arrangements are concealed, so that there is no obvious evidence of the ways in which the various parts are secured together. Sometimes, however, rather than hide the joints, they are made into a feature, and to emphasise this, they are made to be not only functional, but decorative also. This highlights the joint, adds interest, and does not require a lot of extra work. The essence of this variation is to vary the size and spacing of the pins – where the size of these is made less than the thickness of the wood, they have to be cut back on the inner surface. Apart from this, the cutting of the joints is exactly the same as for the standard form of dovetail.

Lap Dovetails

Many of the principles of the common dovetail apply to the lap, as well as other more advanced variations of the joint, such as sloping lines, the spacing of the pins, and the resistance to being taken apart in one direction. The lap

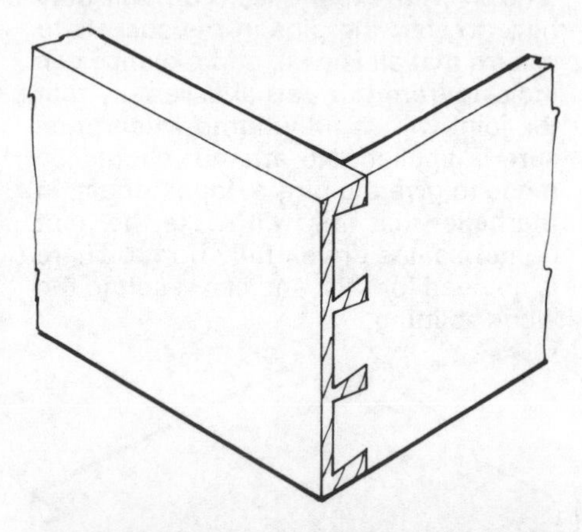

Fig. 108 *(top). Typical lap dovetails as used on drawer fronts.*

Fig. 109 *(above). The lap dovetail joint.*

dovetail is visible on one surface but concealed on the other. This is the joint used more than any other in drawer construction, between the front and the sides, and because of this is sometimes known as the drawer front dovetail. In drawer making, the front is usually thicker than the sides and back, but the joint can just as easily be formed between material of the same thickness. It is also often used for the lower corners of cabinets of box construction, where by the nature of the project, the joint is completely inconspicuous. Here, however, the lower component is usually kept narrower so that its rear edge aligns with the rebate on the cabinet ends. This allows for a back to be fitted in place.

The initial marking out is again carried out with the cutting gauge. The lap is made around a quarter of the thickness of the wood and, as with all joints, the marks made on one piece must correspond with those made on the other. The pins are always formed on the component with the lap, and these are set out as for a through joint.

The first stage of the cutting is to saw down the grain with the dovetail saw, but obviously this can only be partially carried out. The kerf is made to extend from gauge line to gauge line, after which the chisels take over. The wood is

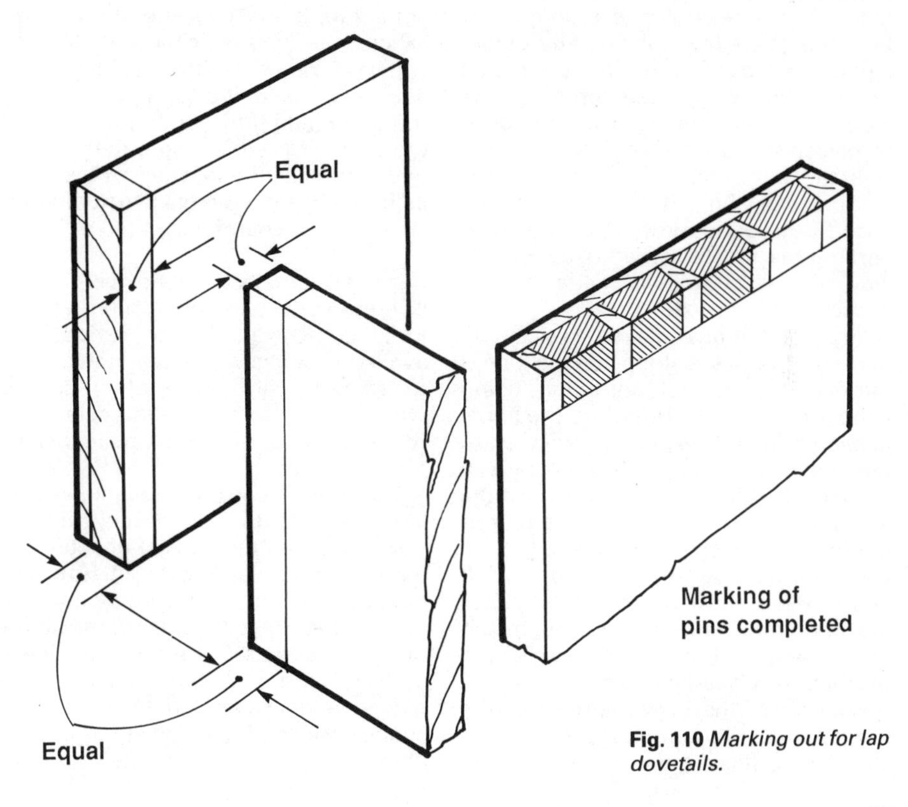

Fig. 110 *Marking out for lap dovetails.*

Fig. 111
Chiselling waste on lap joint.

cramped to the bench, and a bevelled-edge chisel selected which is as large as possible, to fit between the pins. The first cut is a vertical one a little away from the gauge line, followed by a sloping one so as to form a vee-shaped recess. This is repeated three or four times, then the sloping cut is replaced by chiselling horizontally from the end. With the bulk of the waste removed, the vertical chiselling is then completed back to the gauge line. Only the main part of the waste is removed in this way, and no attempt is made to form the actual slopes to the pins.

The wood is now placed vertically in the vice. The waste alongside the pins is removed by careful chiselling using hand pressure only. However, the fibres of the grain still need to be severed at the limit of the waste, which is done by horizontal chiselling. Because of the acute angles involved, ideally a pair of 6 mm (¼ in.) chisel should be ground with their cutting edges angled to left and right to allow chiselling fully into the corners. These chisels are by no means essential, providing a selection of small chisels is available.

Apart from the lower surface of the waste, as the wood remains in the vice, all other surfaces must be totally vertical. The slope of the dovetail is seen only on the end of the wood, all other surfaces must be parallel with, or square to, the face or end of the wood. Where checking is felt necessary, this can be carried out with an adjustable try square of the 'universal' pattern, set so that the blade projects by the extent of the pins. From this stage, the marking and cutting of the tails is just the same as for common dovetails, including the small lead-in chamfers.

Cutting Dovetails using Power

Common dovetails can only be satisfactorily cut by hand. The various jigs available for use with either power drills or routers, rely on rotating cutters, which produce stopped cuts with rounded ends, and are unsuitable for through joints.

The simpler jigs on the market enable lap dovetails to be formed using a power drill, as the special dovetail cutter required is a part of the kit. However, the fit of the joint produced by this type of jig is imperfect. Because of the nature of the cut already mentioned, the lower surface of the waste between the pins is curved, and also angled, because of the shape of the cutter. Against this surface abuts the inner face of the tails. The resultant gap is not large, and is further reduced when pressure forces the components together on assembly. Softwoods, by their very nature, are more accommodating to the shortcomings of the fit than are hardwoods.

The same cutter is used to remove the waste from both parts of the joint, and the jig has pre-determined and non-adjustable spacings of the pins and sockets. This results in a joint where the pins and tails are of equal size, and the layout provides for maximum strength, but least visual appeal. Because of the fixed spacing of the pins across the width of the wood, the most desirable layout cannot always be achieved, with often the two outer pins being either rather large, or somewhat smaller, than the ideal.

What also has to be remembered is that rotating cutters for use in power

Fig. 112 *Simple dovetailing jig in use.*

Fig. 113 *Lap joint formed on simple jig.*

Fig. 114 *The Elu dovetailing jig in use.*

drills cut the wood with reasonable but not high efficiency. The surfaces produced can be a little ragged, especially in certain woods, and there is a danger that corners can be slightly splintered. The joints produced by these jigs can be quite good, but they do have their limitations, and should be regarded as being best suited for occasional work. All cutters of a milling type are best if used in a drill of high speed and adequate power, so that this speed is maintained.

The jigs designed for use with a router are far more sophisticated than those referred to earlier. A special feature is that both pieces of wood are mounted on the jig at the same time, which enables the pins and sockets to be formed in the one operation. Even more important, however, is the way the tails are formed. These have the inner surface rounded and splayed so as to exactly match the curved end of the space between the pins. Thus it is possible to gain a perfect fit of the two parts without any gaps on the inside surfaces, which is a weakness of the simpler forms of jig.

These jigs have a maximum working width of around 300 mm (12 in.), and will tackle wood with a thickness between 12 mm ($\frac{1}{2}$ in.) and 30 mm ($1\frac{13}{16}$ in.). The router gives a far more accurate and smoother cut than do a power drill and cutter, especially when a T.C.T. router cutter is used, and these

Fig. 115 *Rounded pins form perfect fit.*

factors add to the quality of joint produced. However, the spacing of the elements of the joint are fixed, the size of pins always equals the tails, and again, care is needed in the layout of these parts to ensure the outer edges of the joint are in balance without 'partial' pins being produced. It is essential to have a router which is compatible with the jig, although 'mounting plates' can be used with many models.

With all types of jigs used for forming dovetails, full adjustments can be made to both parts of the joint to ensure the actual fit is satisfactory and reasonably tight. It is, however, essential that all adjustments and trials are made prior to starting on the actual workpieces, and spare wood of identical size should be prepared for this purpose.

Apart from these jigs, the only other power tool which can be brought into use is the drill mounted in a stand, and this for lap dovetails. The waste between the pins can be partly bored out, this reduces the amount of chiselling required, but the inital sawing down the grain is still carried out. It is essential to use either a Forstner bit, or a saw-tooth bit, so that the holes can be bored to overlap if needed, but more importantly, that the holes produced are flat bottomed. The depth stop of the stand must be set so that the hole is bored to exact depth so as to maximise the benefit, the extent of the boring being just up to the line.

Fig. 116 *Boring out waste on lap dovetail pins.*

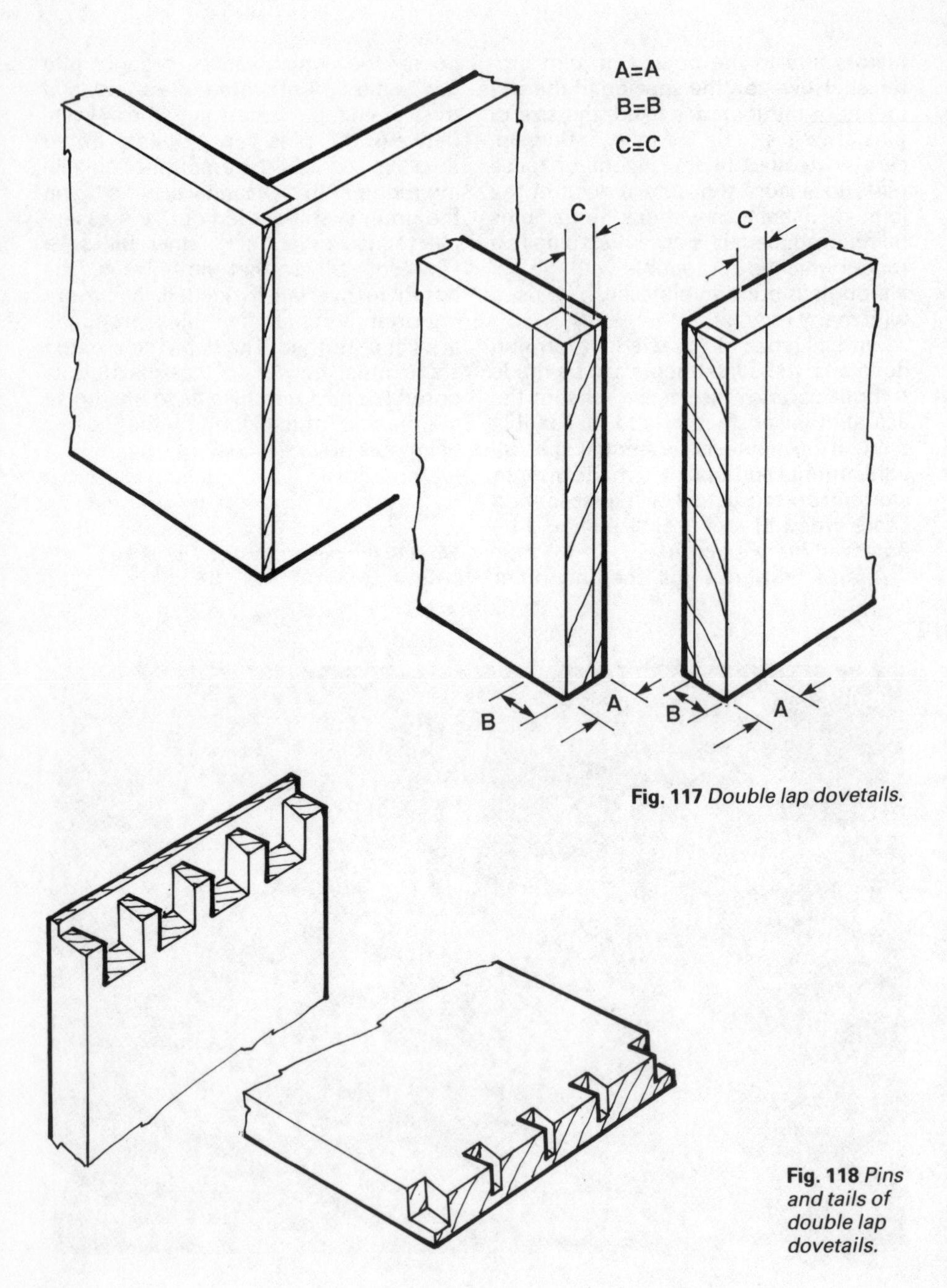

Fig. 117 *Double lap dovetails.*

Fig. 118 *Pins and tails of double lap dovetails.*

Double Lap Dovetails

All signs of the actual dovetail nature of this joint are completely concealed on assembly. It is, therefore, a joint often adopted where both surfaces are visible, especially so in furniture making, when the small area of end grain can be chamfered or rounded over to make it less noticeable. The laps on both pieces are made around a quarter of the thickness of the wood. This joint cannot be formed with the jigs mentioned previously.

As with other forms of corner dovetail, the first stage of the marking out is carried out with the cutting gauge. While the positions of these follow a logical sequence, thought and care are needed because of the accuracy required. It is best to cut the rebate at the ends of the pins before the pins themselves are formed, and this can be completed by any of the methods previously suggested for similar cuts.

The pins are now marked out, with the spacing essentially the same as for through dovetails. Ideally, a modified dovetail template should be made to make the marks within the rebate. The cutting is then carried out in a similar way as for the lap dovetail, and again the boring technique can be used for the removal of much of the waste.

As always with corner dovetails, the marking of the sockets is carried out by pencilling around the pins. Because of the lap on this part of the joint, the dovetail saw can only be used in a restricted way when the cutting is started, as it was for the pins. The removal of the waste must be completed by chisel, although boring out some of the wood can precede this.

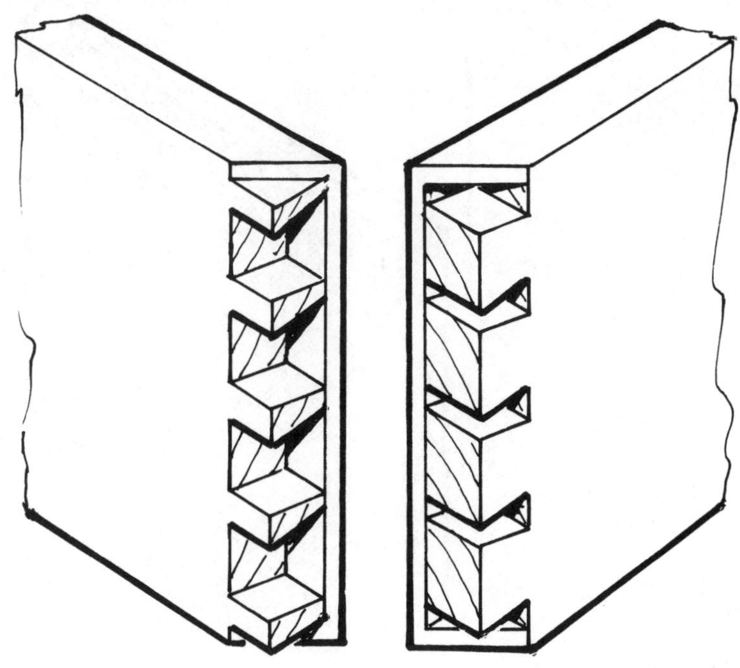

Fig. 119 *The mitre dovetail joint.*

The Mitre Dovetail

The mitre dovetail, when assembled, has the appearance of a plain mitre. It is, therefore, extremely neat, with every part of the joint, except the mitre, being fully concealed. It is the ultimate joint where strength combined with maximum neatness is required, and can be used for any corner situation where these qualities are of paramount importance.

The initial marking out by cutting gauge is actually more straightforward than for the double lap joint, as it is identical for both components. Both have the rebates formed at the ends, these too are identical. However, when the pins are spaced out for the next stage of the marking, those at the edges must be made about 4 mm (3/16 in.) wider than normal, to allow for the outer part of the pins to be mitred.

Cutting the pins is as for the last joint described, after which the mitres on the edges are formed by saw and chisel. The mitre along the lap can be cut partly by chisel, if the wood is not too wide, and this followed by a shoulder plane, or cut entirely by shoulder plane. A good shoulder plane, with a finely set sharp blade is virtually essential for trimming the mitre, and the surfaces being planed must be constantly checked with the mitre square. Extreme caution has to be taken with this stage

Fig. 120 *Marking out for mitre dovetails.*

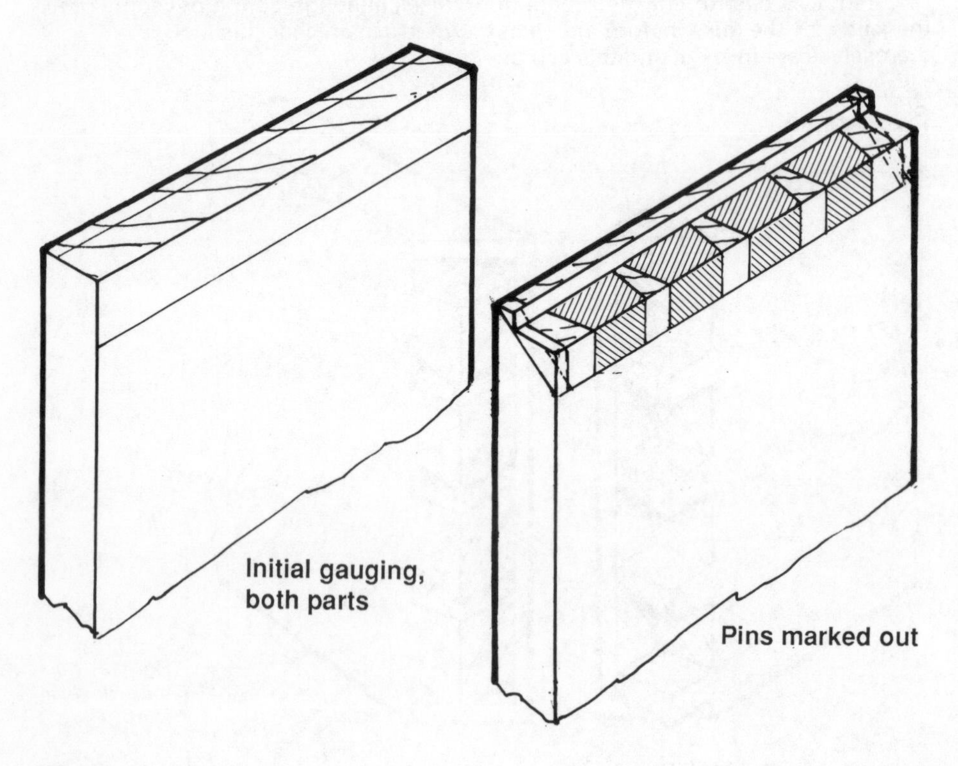

of the joint – a couple of shavings too many on the mitre will result in a gap which is difficult to correct. As an aid to forming this part of the joint, a block of wood with a 45 degree surface can be held behind the piece being planed, and both gripped in the vice. The sloping surface of the block must be level with the finished line of the mitre, and thus act as a guide for the shoulder plane.

The pins are marked and formed as for the double lap variation, and the mitre prepared in a similar way to the first part of the joint. This joint, more than any other, needs practising before attempting on an important project.

CHAPTER 9

DOWEL JOINTS

Although the use of dowelling is quite an old method of jointing wood, it has grown in popularity in more recent years. The power drill, the development of dowelling jigs, and the increased use of faced chipboard have all contributed to the wider use of dowelling techniques. Dowelling can be used for the joints in framing assemblies in solid wood, and also for carcase and box constructions – especially if they are of chipboard, for which it is particularly suitable.

While the principle of dowelling is quite simple, the making of a good dowel joint is not quite as easy as might at first appear, especially if the joint is being prepared without a jig. Carefully made and properly assembled, the joint can be totally satisfactory.

Dowelling is readily available in lengths up to 2240 mm (96 in.), and in diameters from 3 mm (⅛ in.) to 25 mm (1 in.) and even more. However, for dowel joints, sizes of 6 mm, 8 mm, and 10 mm (¼ in., 5/16 in. and ⅜ in.) are the ones most likely to be chosen, and occasionally 13 mm (½ in.). Although in theory, dowelling can be bought in metric and imperial sizes, it is not always the exact diameter it should be, can vary from batch to batch, and is not always perfectly round. Dowelling is usually made from beech or ramin, both strong and straight grained timbers. It is also possible to obtain packs of prepared dowels. These have a serrated surface, with both ends chamfered for ease of entry into the holes. However, these dowels tend to be a little on the short side, perfectly suitable for joints in fairly thin boards which includes most faced chipboards, but not quite ideal for framing joints.

Whether a jig is being used or not, a power drill makes boring the holes quick and easy, and the lip-and-spur bit is the pattern widely used for preparing dowel holes. These bits are also available in both metric and imperial sizes, and it is essential to ensure the bit correctly matches the jig. While there might be both inaccuracy and tolerance in the dowelling, this is not so with the jigs and bits, which are produced to high levels of accuracy. The holes which guide the bits within the jig are lined with hardened steel bushes – oversize bits will not fit, and smaller ones will not be properly guided.

When boring into the face of a board, it is usually best to bore the holes as deep as possible, without even the tip of the bit piercing the reverse surface. Some kind of depth stop is therefore needed on the bit. These take various forms and are sometimes included with the dowelling jig. The simplest is a heavy duty elastic band, positioned on the bit so as to limit the extent of the boring. However, these should be taken as guides only as they can become disturbed in use, and frequent checking is therefore essential. The steel collar depth gauge is more positive – this is locked to the bit with a grub screw but the size of the collar must match the bit. Home made stops are quickly made. An oddment of wood about 19 mm – 25 mm (¾ in. – 1 in.) square is bored down its centre, and cut to length so that the amount of projection of the bit through the wood equals the depth of hole required.

FRAMING JOINT

The simplest form of dowel joint is between two framing members which meet at right angles, and where two dowels are used. When a jig is not being used, the joint must be fully marked out to show the layout of all the holes. Wherever possible, a gauge is used to make the necessary lines, all three lines for the two holes can be made by gauge on the component to be bored at its end. The corresponding component has to be marked by try square and gauge, and checking the marking of one member against the other should always take place. The spacing of the dowels when used for framing are the same on the outer members as they are on intermediate components. It helps if extra length is left on the stiles to prevent the risk of splitting, which is sawn off and levelled after assembly.

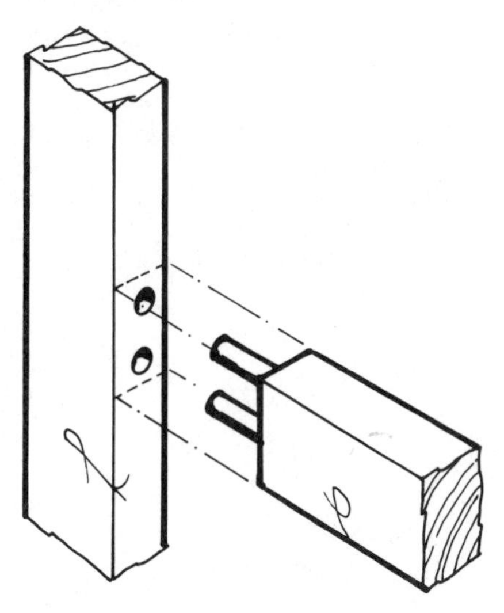

Fig. 121 *Basic form of dowel joint.*

I have found it helps if the actual centre of the holes is emphasised by making a small indentation with a bradawl, preferably of the birdcage type which has pointed ends. This ensures more positive location of the tip of the bit when boring takes place, and promotes accuracy.

The diameter of the dowel to use should in most cases be about half the thickness of the wood, or the most convenient size below this. Where the two components are of unequal thickness, the diameter of dowel must be related to the thinner piece. As the dowel needs to penetrate into each piece of wood by approximately 25 mm (1 in.), the holes are bored about 3 mm – 4 mm (⅛ in. – 3/16 in.) deeper, as it is essential to have some clearance at the ends of the dowel to prevent fouling on assembly.

The number of dowels used in a joint clearly relates to the width of the material. Framing assemblies, by their nature, tend to be made of wood of fairly small section, around 50 mm by 25 mm (2 in.×1 in.) being typical for most applications. Wood of 75 mm (3 in.)

width would require three dowels, and as the width increases further, the aim should be to space the dowels at around 44 mm – 50 mm (1¾ in – 2 in.) centres. On wood of fairly small section in particular, a balance has to be made between not making the holes too close nor too large, which would tend to weaken the wood, and the strenth and support offered by the dowels themselves.

DOWELLING FOR BOX CONSTRUCTIONS

On box type constructions, the wood is likely to be fairly wide but relatively thin, with the holes being made into the ends of one part but the face of the other. The centre line for the holes to be made on the face of the component is made with the try square and pencil, and on the end of the other member by gauge. The spacing of the hole is best indicated with the help of a marking aid. This is simply a strip of wood around 25 mm by 13 mm (1 in.×½ in.) on which is marked the width of the material along with lines indicating the spacing of the dowels. This strip is then used instead of the rule, thus almost eliminating the risk of wrongly positioned holes.

Where the dowel joint is used for the upper corner of a carcase, it helps if the top surfaces are not made actually level, but with a deliberate step introduced. This is largely because if they were made level, the slightest movement in the wood subsequent to completing the project would result in a slight mis-alignment appearing. The step conceals this possibility, the difference in levels being made about 1.5 mm (1⁄16 in.). This also overcomes the problems of aiming to make the outer surfaces flush, and possibly hav-

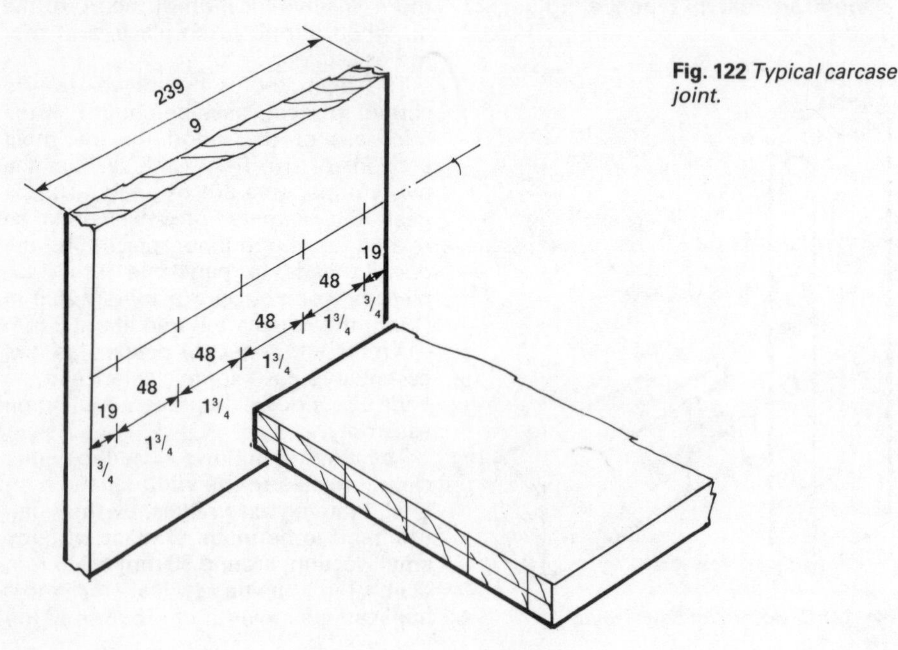

Fig. 122 *Typical carcase joint.*

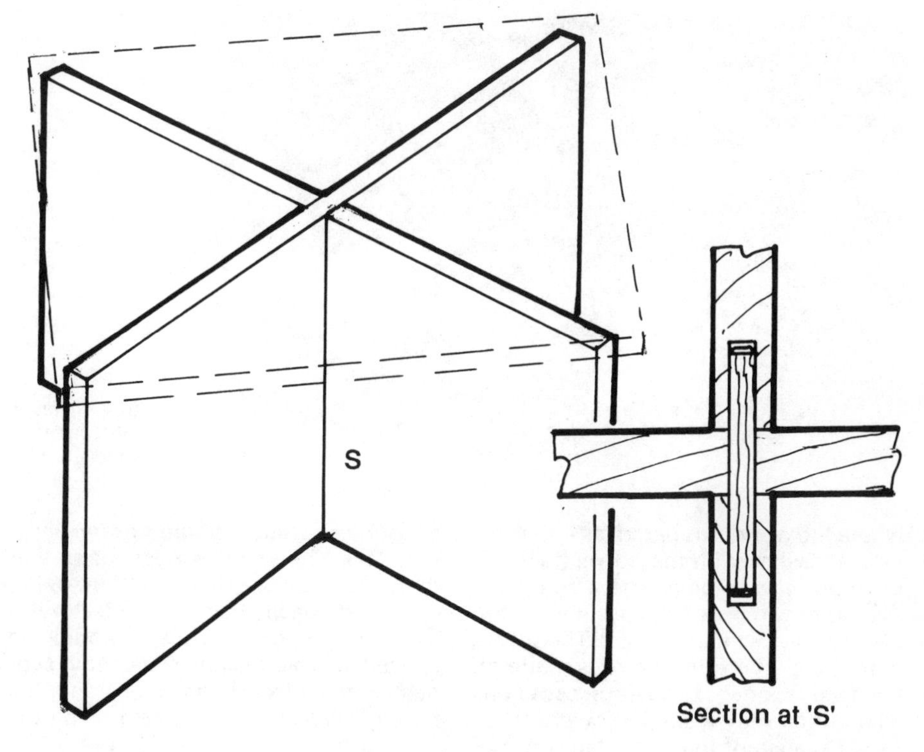

Fig. 123 *Dowelling three components.*

ing to carry out final levelling to achieve this, when the material is a chipboard with a very thin veneer or melamine face.

THREE-WAY JOINT

Sometimes the dowel joint is used between three, rather than the more usual two components. I have used the three-way dowel joint on a number of occasions, such as for a simple low table where the 'legs' are made up of one large and two small pieces of board material and one joint connects all three, and on another, where the top rails of a dining table had to cross at 90 degrees. As an alternative to using halvings to joint the wood where they intersected, one rail was made continuous, the other formed as two halves, and all three pieces jointed with one set of dowels.

DOWELLED MITRES

The corners of frames can be mitred and the mitres strengthened by dowels, and this offers a means of jointing for assemblies such as small doors. The method allows for rebates and moulded edges to be formed on the wood without these directly affecting the joint. It is never very satisfactory to use normal dowel framing joints described earlier,

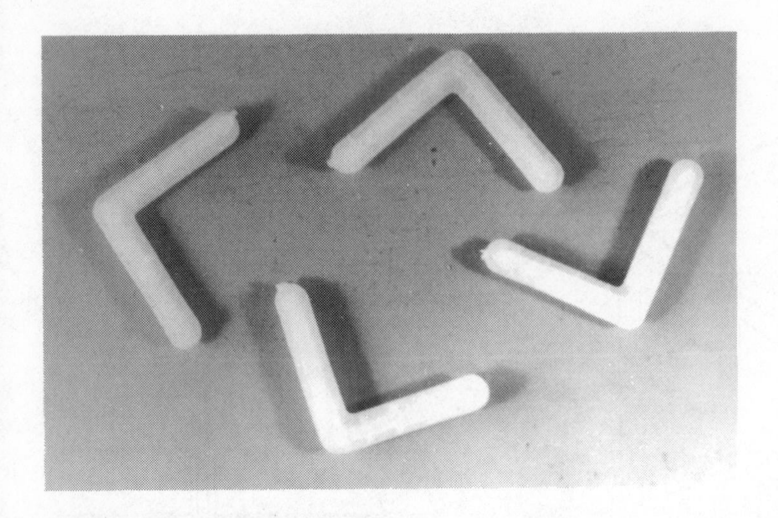

Fig. 124 *Plastic right-angled dowels.*

where the wood is rebated, as either the rebate clashes with the dowel holes, or the wood has to be cut-back alongside the holes in order to provide a flat surface level with the rebate. The corner mitre joint where the mitre is made on the face is one of the rare occasions when often only a single dowel can be used because of the restricted width of the wood. An alternative to the normal dowel, where in mitres the holes are made at 90 degrees to the mitred surfaces, is to use right-angled dowels, for which the holes are bored parallel to the edges of the material.

Right-angled dowels are made of plastic, and are available in one size only, 25 mm × 25 mm × 6 mm (1 in. × 1 in. × ¼ in). They have a ribbed surface to assist the gluing. These dowels have a particular application for box constructions with mitred corners, as the mitre is on the edge of the wood rather than the face, as for a framing mitre joint mentioned earlier.

When using these dowels, it is necessary to bore the holes before forming the mitres, otherwise difficulties will be encountered and the necessary accuracy lost. The wood is best cut so that there is 6 mm–12 mm (¼ in.–½ in.) waste at each end, and the mitre marked in pencil. Holes should be spaced at the distances already suggested for box construction, and the boring made either freehand or by the aid of a jig.

Only when the holes have been bored is the waste removed at the ends to form the mitres, and these trimmed as required on the mitre shooting board. When assembling this joint, a resin type adhesive will give a better bond on the plastic dowel than a PVA adhesive.

TENON AND DOWEL

This joint is used where two rails are jointed into a leg, with a mortise and tenon being used on one side and dowels on the other. Its particular application is for dining chairs, especially of the traditional pattern. The tenons are used on the seat side rails, and the dowels on the front and back rails. The advantage of this combination is that the dowels also provide pins through the tenons, thus locking the joint very solidly together. Considerable strength is required in a chair, especially if there are no lower rails, because of the racking effect on the joints when the user tips the chair back and balances only on the rear legs.

Although the dowel holes in the legs are initially bored before any assembly takes place, further boring will be necessary before the dowelled rails can be added. With most chairs, it is usual to first glue-up the legs and side rails as sub-assemblies. At this stage, the dowel holes in the legs will need to be completed by boring through the tenons of the side rails, so that the dowels will penetrate and provide the locking effect.

Fig. 125 *Tenoned and dowelled chair leg joint.*

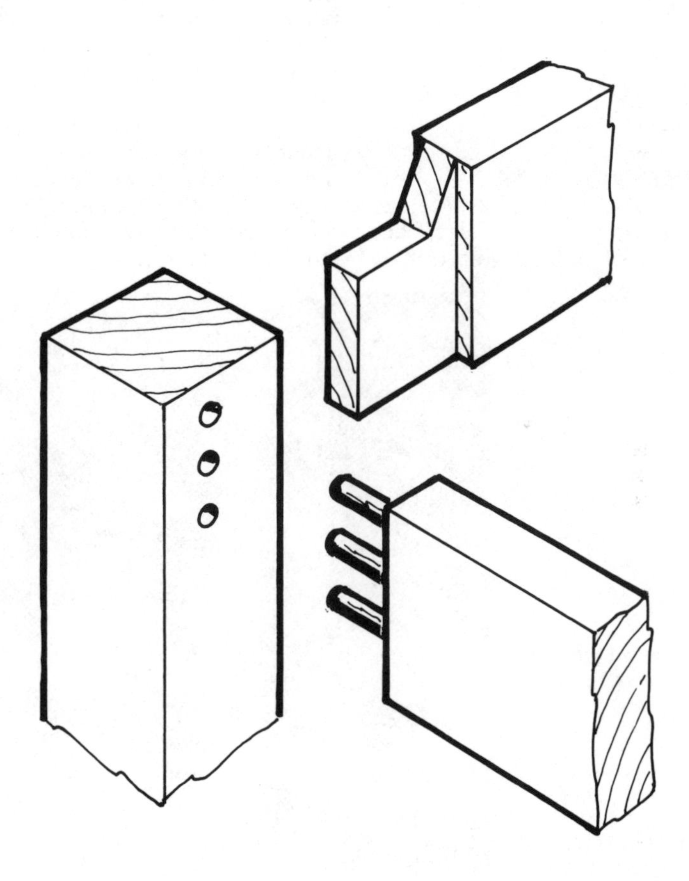

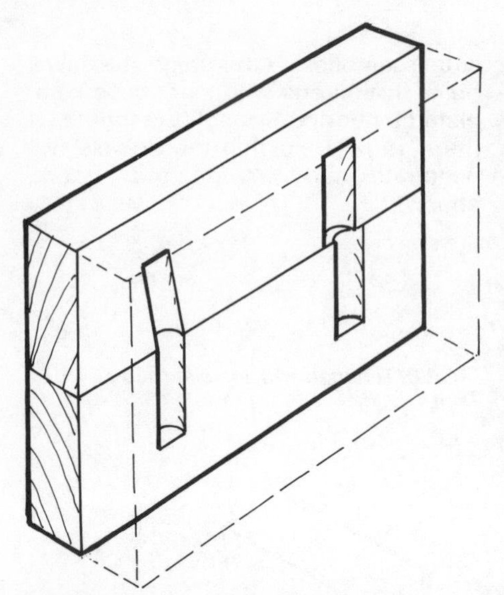

Fig. 126 *Misalignment of holes.*

BORING HOLES WITHOUT A JIG

Few people these days are likely to use a brace for boring the holes, but whether this tool or a power drill is being used, particular care is needed when used entirely freehand. Misalignment of the holes can easily take place because of careless boring; two common errors are holes which are not exactly opposite one another, and holes which are not bored perpendicular to the surface. These possible errors underline the need for accuracy when marking out, and why it is worthwhile to use a bradawl before boring. While the eye has to be relied upon to a large extent to ensure the holes are square to the surface, it helps if the tip given when hand mortising is adopted, that is, standing a try square on-end near the work and against which the bit can be aligned.

Even when a jig is not being used, it is a considerable advantage to use the drill in a drill stand. This ensures the holes are being bored at right angles to the surface, and in addition the depth stop of the stand can be used.

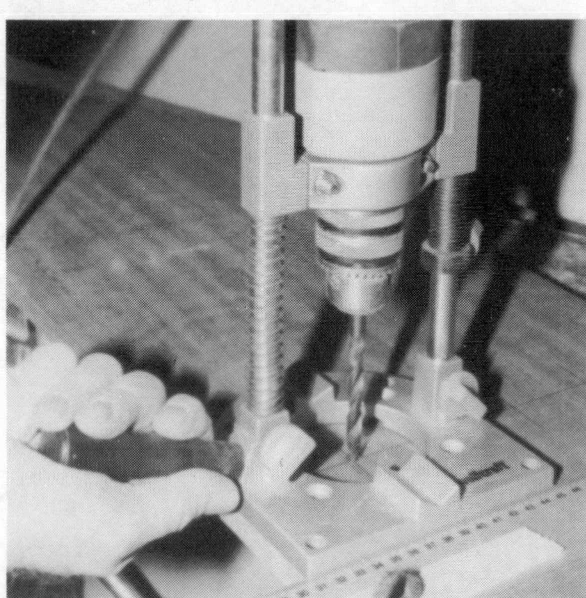

Fig. 127 *Preparing dowel holes with drill guide.*

A drill guide can also be of benefit when the holes are being prepared in fairly wide material. The guide allows for the holes to be bored square into the wood, and the depth can be readily controlled. When used on the face of the board, alignment of all the holes is easily achieved by using a guide secured to the wood – a router guide or Wolfcraft Combinal being ideal. The drill guide can also be used when boring into the edges or ends of the board, the aligning pins straddle the wood, are kept tight against opposite surfaces, and ensures the holes are central. The drill guide is not suitable for boring into the ends of narrow material because of insufficient surface to control the guide.

PREPARING THE DOWELS

Generally, 'dowelling' refers to the long length of the material, and 'dowel' to the short, prepared piece, as used in the joint. In the furniture industry, they are known as dowel pins. Some preparation of the dowelling is required in order to produce satisfactory dowels. A small groove is needed along the length, to allow excess glue and trapped air to escape during assembly. A small circular saw can be used for this, by passing a length of dowelling over the blade when set low in the table. Another way is to make a dowel groover. Holes are bored in a block of hardwood to match popular sizes of dowel, and screws driven into the sides of the block so that the tips just penetrate into the holes. The block is gripped in the vice, and cut lengths of dowel are driven through the appropriate hole. Adjustment is made on the size of the groove by turning the screw slightly, the efficiency being improved if the end

Fig. 128 *Preparing dowels in grooving block.*

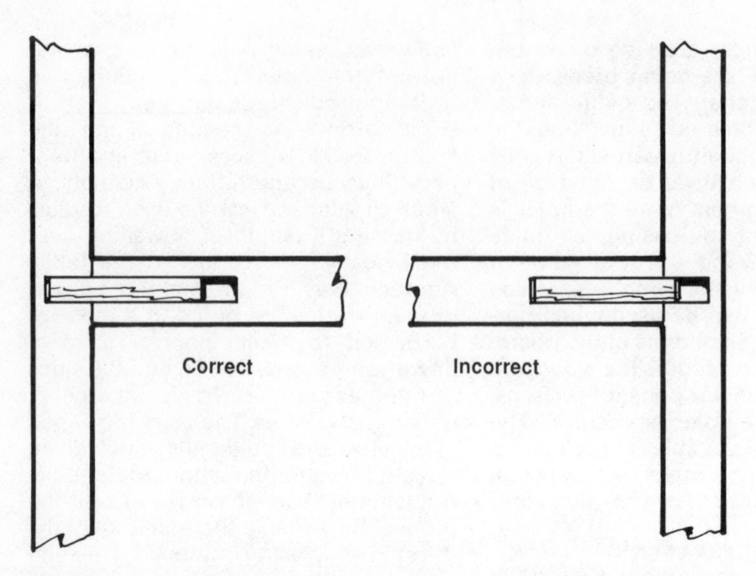

Fig. 129 *Insertion of dowels into thin material.*

of the screw is first filed to create a pyramidal point.

The ends of the dowel need pointing to a small extent, to allow easy entry when assembled. A special tool is available for this, and they can also be quickly pointed by chisel. A disc sander is also a very satisfactory way, rotating the dowel in the fingers as it is held against the disc.

Assembling

It is important that adhesive is used on all surfaces coming into contact, including the holes. Initially the dowels are driven into the holes in one of the components, and with fairly thin boards it is important into which member the dowels are first driven. Where there are holes on the face of the board, the dowels should be driven into these first. This ensures maximum penetration into the shallower hole. When driving the dowels into thin material, the work must be fully supported directly below the holes, or the dowels can be knocked completely through, especially if of chipboard.

DOWELLING JIGS

There is no shortage of these on the market, all work well within their limitations but their adaptability varies. Many have been designed with chipboard in mind, and are not really suitable for general application. The simplest are of plastic, and allow for just one hole of a fixed diameter to be bored at one time. The hole for the bit is lined with a steel bush, and when the jig is used on the edge or end of the board, the hole is automatically positioned in the centre, and this cannot be varied. Rather better plastic jigs allow for the boring the three most popular sizes of dowel, 6 mm, 8 mm and 10 mm, but again only one hole can be bored at one setting.

With these simpler jigs, one set of holes forming a joint is bored, dowels temporarily inserted, then these projecting dowels used to guide the jig while the second series of holes is bored. With care the jigs work well, but speed of working is relatively slow because of the frequent re-positioning needed.

Better jigs are of metal, have their own built-in clamps, and again allow for the three common sizes of holes to be made. However, the jigs are designed so that each pair of holes required for the joint can be made at the one setting. Not only do these jigs speed up the work because of the reduced number of positions the jig has to take up on the

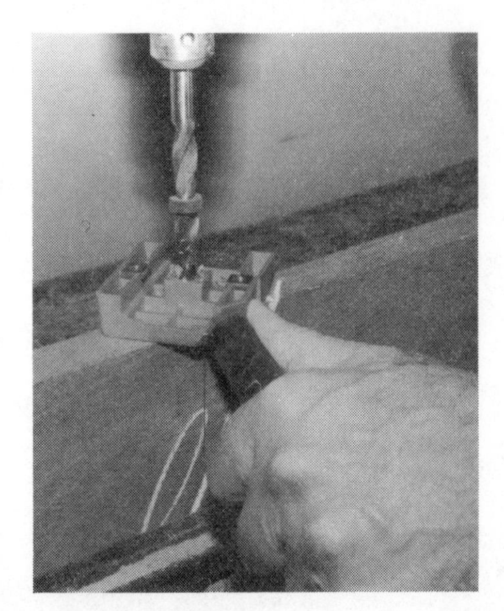

Fig. 130 *Simple single hole jig in use.*

Fig. 131 *Wolfcraft all-metal jig with spacer.*

wood, but the alignment of the holes is better controlled. In addition, these jigs can cope with a wider range of applications, including the joints required for framing assemblies.

Far and away the best dowelling jig available is the Marples M148. This is highly versatile, and allows for boring holes for almost every possible application. The basic kit allows for boring two holes in wood up to 150 mm (6 in.) wide, but extra guide rods enable material up to 450 mm (18 in.) wide to be tackled, and with additional drill guides mounted on the rods, all the holes needed for a multiple dowelled joint can be made at the one setting. In addition, the drill bushes within the guides are interchangeable, so that holes of various sizes, either metric or imperial can be made.

The M148 will cope with material up to any reasonable thickness, and the holes can be made centrally or in any other position. This jig is of professional quality and application, and only the minimum of preliminary marking out is required. Indeed, for certain types of dowel joints, no marking at all is needed, as correct use of the jig will automatically govern the exact location of the holes.

Fig. 132 *The Spiralux all-metal jig.*

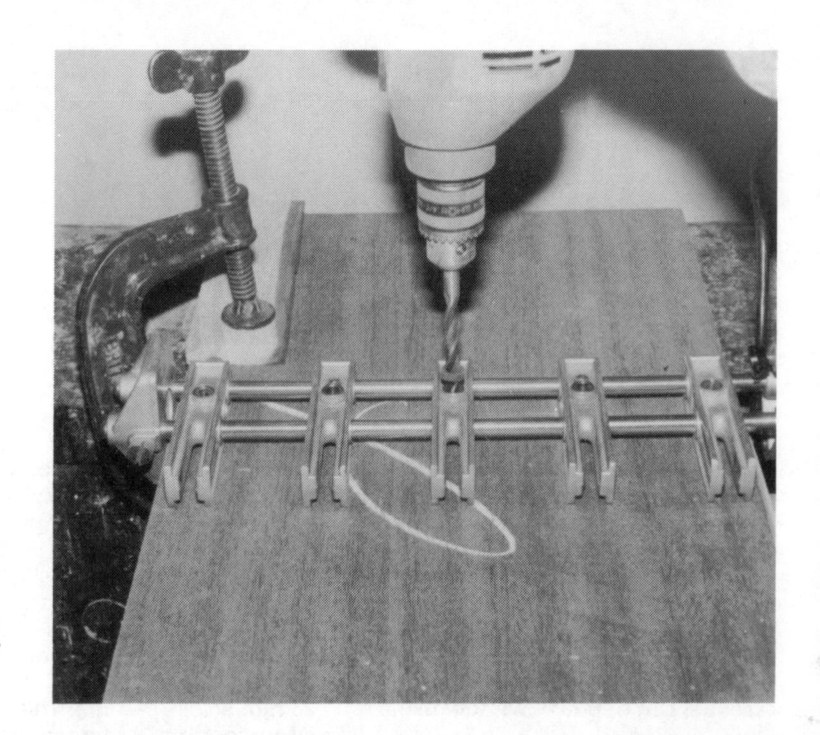

Fig. 133 *The Marples 148 at end of material.*

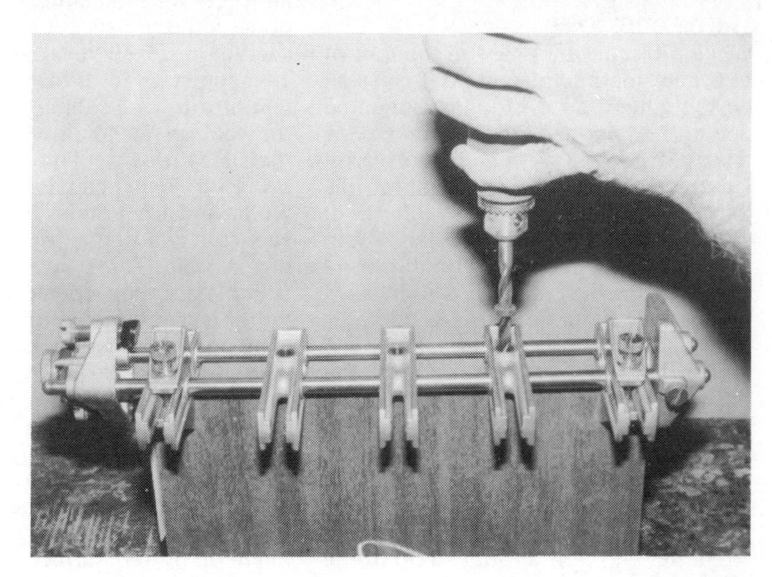

Fig. 134 *The jig at the end of the material.*

CHAPTER 10

MISCELLANEOUS JOINTS

Many joints featured in old woodworking books were rarely used, and then only for specialized applications, and can really be regarded as obsolete. As certain joints have slipped into oblivion, a small number of others have appeared, although these have been introduced largely because of the developments in machines and power tools, and in the cutters which are an essential part of power woodworking.

THE BISCUIT JOINT

While a biscuit joint can be thought of as a 'new' method of jointing, it can also be thought of as a form of elongated dowel, and indeed is also known as biscuit dowelling. A specialized biscuit jointing power tool is essential for this joint, which in essence is a form of small but highly refined circular saw. In use, the tool is positioned on the wood and the handle raised, this in turn plunges the blade into the wood so as to make a cut of segmental outline. The tool is fully adjustable to control the position and depth of cut, with the width governed by the thickness of the blade.

The 'biscuits', specially made from hardwood, are cut so that the grain runs diagonally to provide maximum strength, and are produced in three sizes. One of the secrets of this jointing method lies in the fact that during manufacture these biscuits are compressed slightly. When glued in place, water from the adhesive is absorbed by the biscuit, this causes slight swelling, and thus the biscuit is further tightened in the saw cut. The sizes of the biscuits range from approximately 45 mm × 16 mm (1¾ in. × ⅝ in.), to 63 mm × 25 mm (2½ in. × 1 in.). The thickness of all three are the same so as to correspond with the saw cut made. Although seemingly of elliptical shape, the curved edges of all sizes of the biscuits conform to the outline of the blade of the tool so as to provide a fit which matches the saw cut made.

Biscuit joints can be used in solid wood and man-made boards, and the saw cuts can be made in any direction of the grain. The system is particularly suitable for box constructions, but is rather less adaptable for frame assemblies unless the wood is at least 50 mm (2 in.) wide.

Elu produce a biscuit jointer which is a precision tool and can be adjusted to fine tolerances. Correctly used, it can create joints of a high level of accuracy and effectiveness, and the adapter plate included allows for the saw cuts to be made on mitred surfaces. Although the

Fig. 135 *The Elu biscuit jointer.*

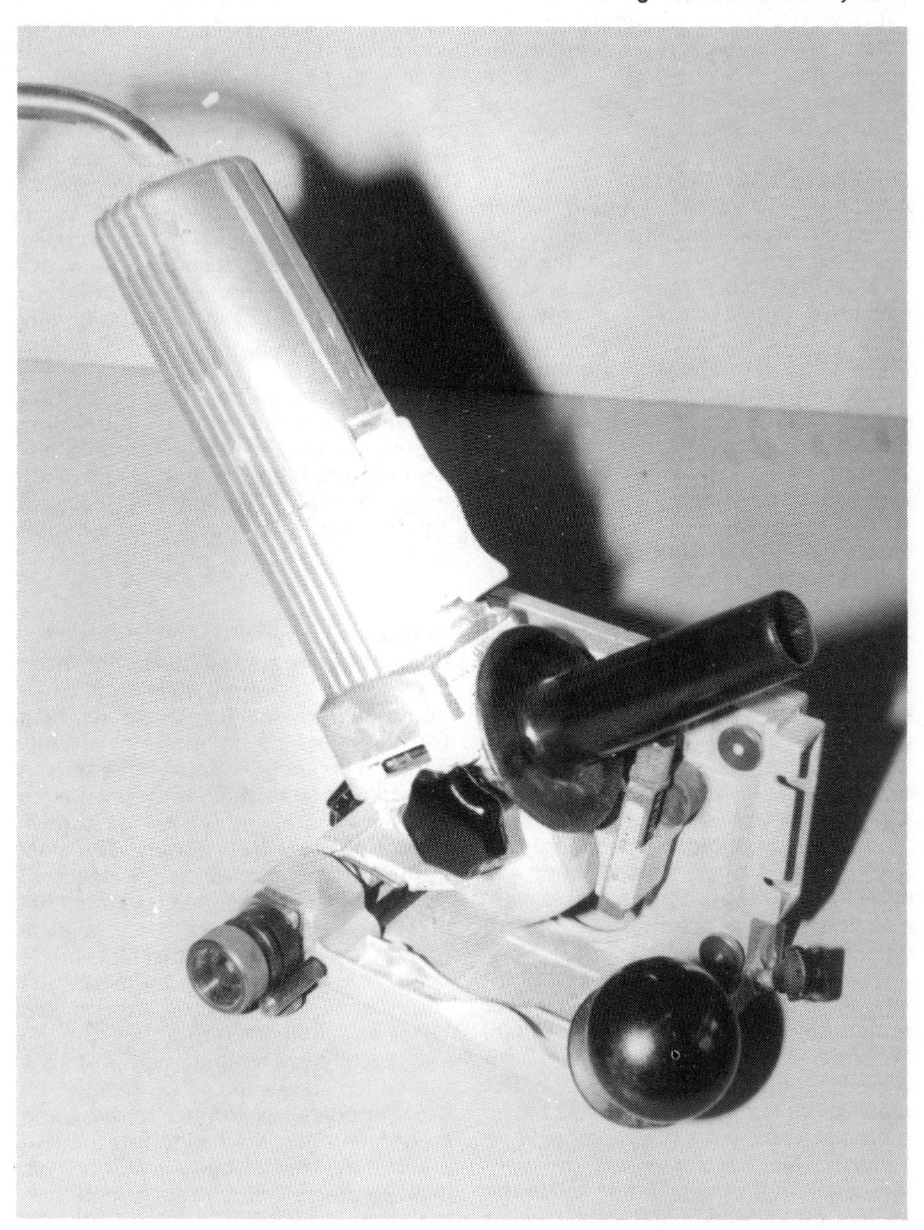

biscuit jointer is used to make plunge cuts only when held stationary, in order to form the curved kerf required for the biscuit, it can also be used as a grooving saw for making through or stopped grooves in any direction of the grain.

SPECIAL ROUTER CUTTERS

Additional ways of jointing when widening wood depend entirely on router cutters. In these cases, the glue area of the two edges in contact is increased considerably, and only one cutter is required to produce both parts of the joint. The one with the multiple interlocking projections is called a finger joint, and the other a combined tongue and groove, but these names are not to be confused with similar names used elsewhere.

The table-leaf, or rule joint, is employed between the main top of a table and the folding leaves as used on gate-leg and similar tables of traditional design. The rule joint allows for the ovolo moulding to be formed on all the edges of the central, fixed part of the top, and continued around the outer edges of the leaves. The inner edges of these are then radiused to match the ovolo, and the results are that better alignment is provided when the leaves are raised compared with a plain joint, and there is no gap created when the leaves are lowered. Special 'table flap' hinges are required for such a table, a modified form of back flap.

When first introduced, the rule joint was formed by a matching pair of wooden moulding planes, and can still be formed by hand using a combination plane with the appropriate blades. For speed of working, accuracy, and better cutting across the grain, a router is to be preferred, and special cutters are available enabling perfect fitting between the two parts. Several different sizes of paired cutters are produced, and they can of course be used independently for moulding and coving work.

One joint not mentioned in the chapter on corner joints is the one combining a rebate with a mitre, such a joint being completely concealed on the outer faces. While it can be formed by hand methods, it lends itself to being cut by router for which matching pairs of cutters are produced. Each cutter forms the full profile required for each half of the joint, and will cut in any thickness up to a maximum of 19 mm (3/4 in.).

Apart from the rule joint, the other cutters mentioned require a heavy duty router, and the use of a router table. It is also essential that the wood is properly prepared, with straight edges and square ends – the router cutters do not do this as a part of the profiling.

SECRET SCREWING

Boarded doors are often used for furniture of the 'country' style, and such doors require the boards to be held together on the inside by battens. Rather than simply screw the battens to the boards, a far neater method is to use secret screwing where the screws cannot be seen on assembly. The slots in the battens into which the heads of the screws are embedded comprise the hole, made rather larger than the heads of the screws, and the actual slots made about 13 mm (1/2 in.) long, with the width equal to the shank of the screw. These are initially formed by drilling and chiselling. The undercutting to the slot which allows the screw head to be accommodated is formed by adapting an ordinary screw so as to form a simple cutter. This is done by filing the head to create two cutting edges, and the screw is then fixed in the chuck of a

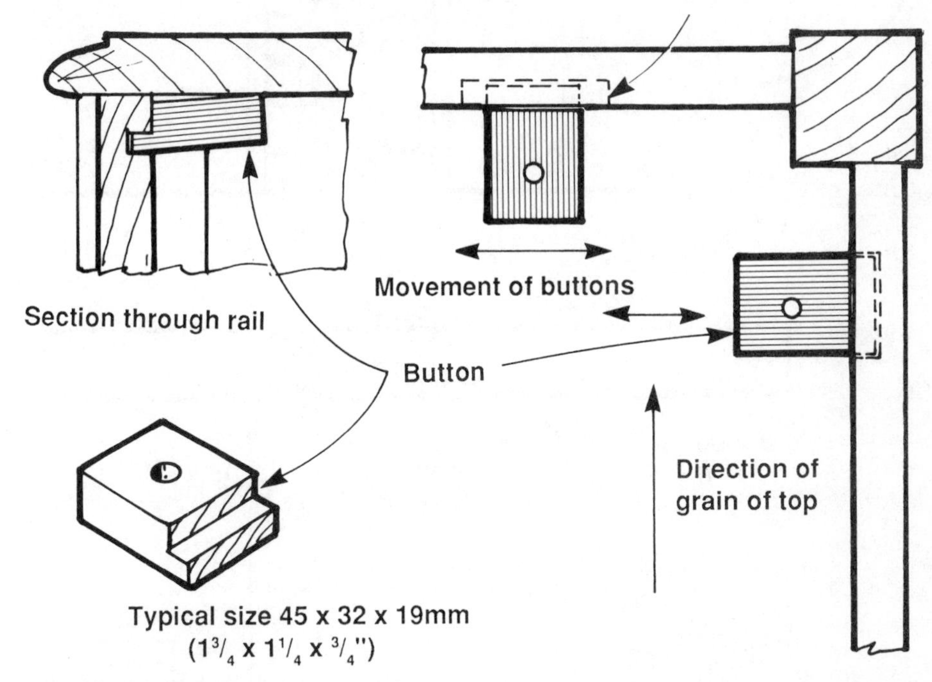

Fig. 136 *Traditional buttons.*

power drill so that the amount projecting is marginally less than the depth of the slots so far prepared. In most cases, this needs to be around 10 mm (⅜ in.). The screw-cutter is inserted into the hole, and sideways pressure on the drill allows the undercutting to be formed. The ends of the chuck jaws must rest on the surface of the wood, to ensure uniformity of cutting, and likewise all the screws inserted into the boards must project by an equal amount.

When secret-screwed components are being assembled, it is essential that the parts are in close contact, then the batten carefully tapped home. A little glue at one end of the batten ensures positive retention, and also that the door will keep square. Secret screwing has many applications other than for door battens.

BUTTONS

Reference has been made a number of times about the movement of wood across the grain, because of the amount of moisture present in the wood which in turn depends partly on the location of the project. For furniture, shrinkage is more likely than swelling, and the wider the wood then the greater the amount of movement. Solid table tops must be secured to their underframes in such a way that movement can take place.

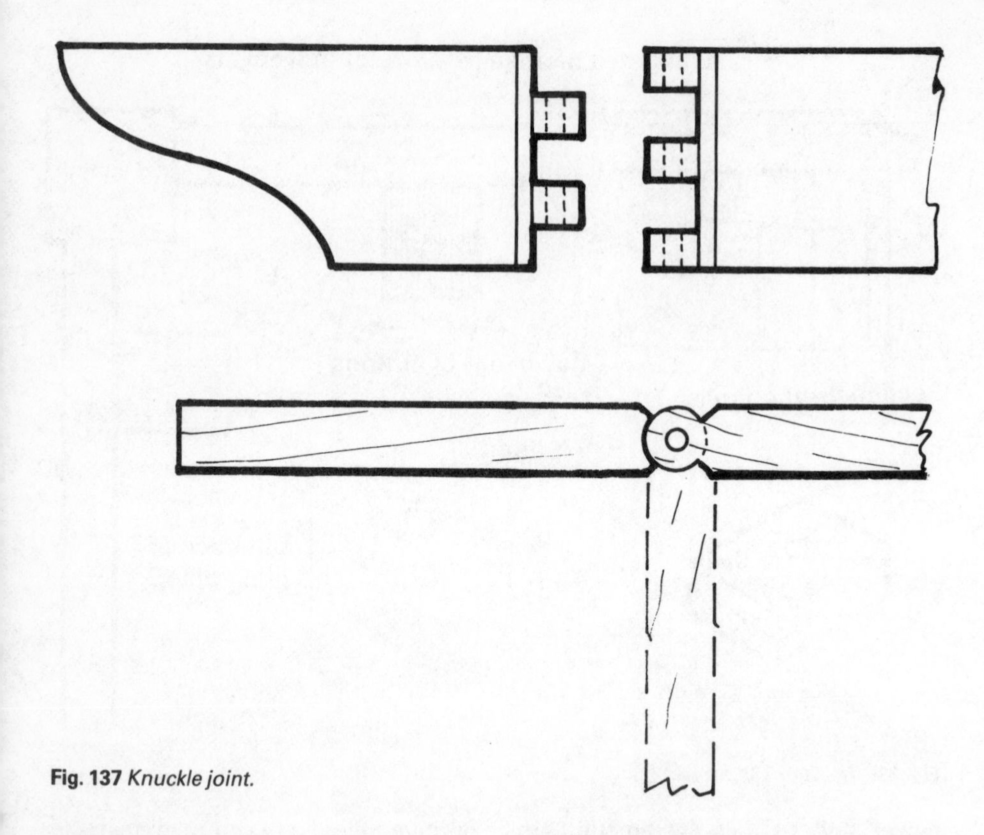

Fig. 137 *Knuckle joint.*

Failure to do so can readily lead to splitting of the top.

The traditional way of securing table tops is by the use of 'buttons'. The tongue on these engage in mortises formed in the rails, and are made wider than the tongue to allow for the movement to take place. It is also important that there is initially a slight gap between the button and the underside of the top, so that the screw can effectively pull the top into close contact with the rails.

KNUCKLE JOINT

The knuckle joint is really a form of wooden hinge, and its particular uses are for the brackets which support the flaps of small extending tables, and for the pivotting legs of semi-circular tables which open up to be a full circle.

Five knuckles are usually incorporated into the joint, and the rather better arrangement is to have the larger number of knuckles on the fixed part. Note that the cut-away sections need to be slightly hollowed so as to match the rounded end of the knuckle, and the inner limits of the joint control the extent of the opening. Old examples of these joints show that a dowel was the actual pin, but nowadays a steel pin is preferred which provides a longer life and stronger joint. A steel pin of smaller

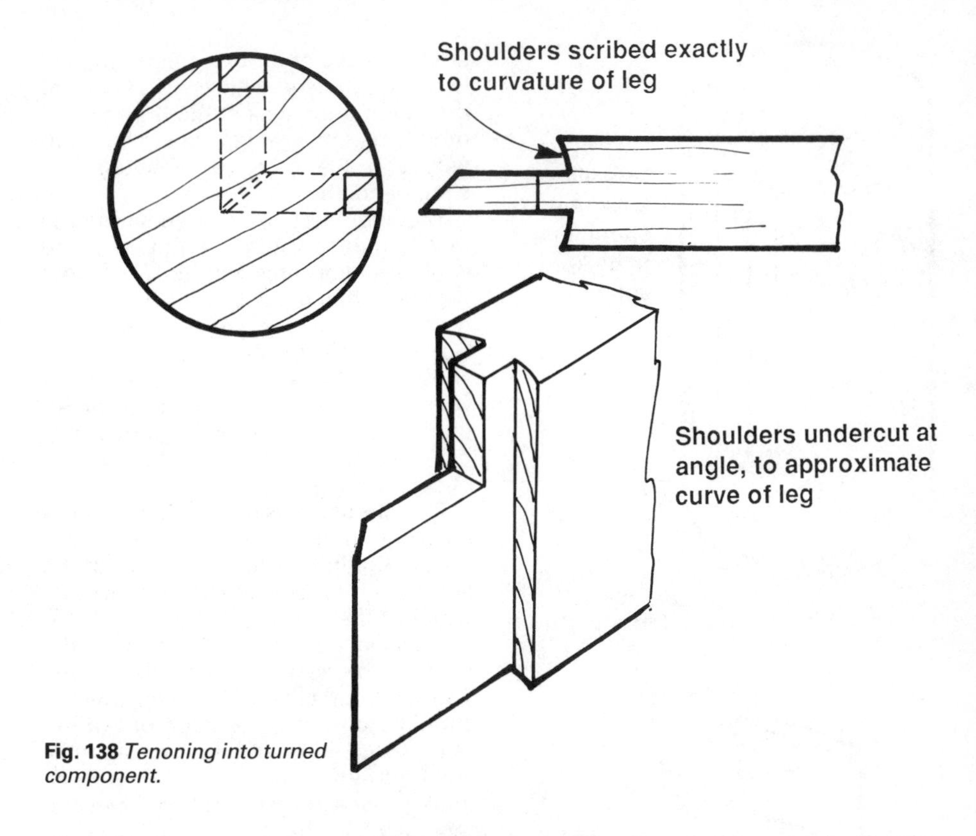

Fig. 138 *Tenoning into turned component.*

diameter than a wooden dowel can be used, and thus smaller holes are required.

Lines should be squared around the components to indicate the limits of the joint, the centres for the holes marked on the edges, along with the arcs required for the rounding of the knuckles. The sloping inner ends of the joint should be marked with a sliding bevel. The angle will vary according to the extent of the opening which is required, but will be 45 degrees for a joint to be opened to a right angle. A saw cut is made at the 'vee' part of the joint, and the rounding formed by a small plane at the outer end, and a shoulder plane for the remainder. The holes are bored at this stage.

After the initial rounding, the knuckles are marked with a mortise gauge as for a comb joint, and cut in a similar way with tenon and coping saws, with a chisel used for trimming the inner ends. Final trimming and sanding of the curved surfaces of the knuckles takes place when the two halves are fitted together.

JOINTS FOR TURNED COMPONENTS

Where rails are tenoned into a turned component such as a leg, then some adjustment is needed to the joint in order to make a satisfactory fit. There

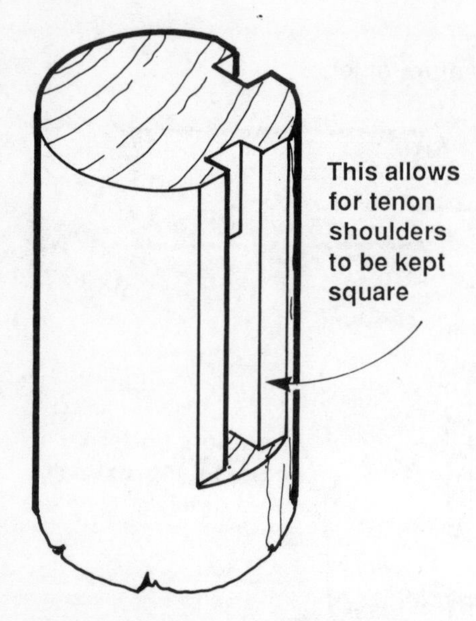

Fig. 139 *Modification to mortise in turned component.*

are two ways of ensuring that the joint is properly made with the shoulder of the tenon tight against the leg – one is modifying the area adjacent to the mortise, and the other is adjusting the shoulder of the rail.

The shoulders need to be scribed to match the curvature of the leg, and while in theory this can be carried out with a scribing gouge, such a cut is never easy over a fairly wide rail. A simpler variation is to undercut the shoulder slightly when this is being cut with the saw. A very close approximation can fairly easily be gained with better consistency than can be produced by gouge.

The alternative is to form flat surfaces adjacent to the mortise to ensure a proper seating for the shoulders of the tenons. It is essential to have the overall width of the flat surface on the turned component equal to the thickness of the rails, or the fit will not be satisfactory. The usual practice of forming a small shoulder on the lower edge of the top rail, or both edges of intermediate rails, is of no advantage with this type of joint. It is also essential to have the mortises on the centre line of each adjacent surface, as forming the mortises off-centre means unnecessarily complicating the joint. The mortises are far easier to cut before turning.

Often the turned component has to be fixed into a rail, rather than the opposite way round, and this is usually done by forming a tenon on the end of the turned member. This is normally known as a spigot, and is usually held in place with a wedge. This should be driven in at right angles to the grain of

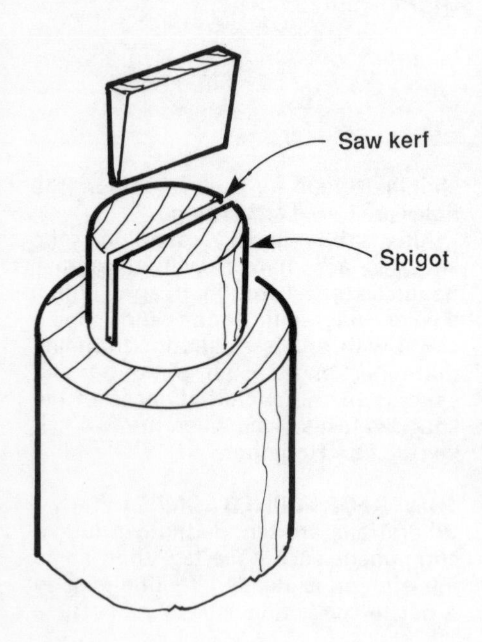

Fig. 140 *Turned tenon or spigot.*

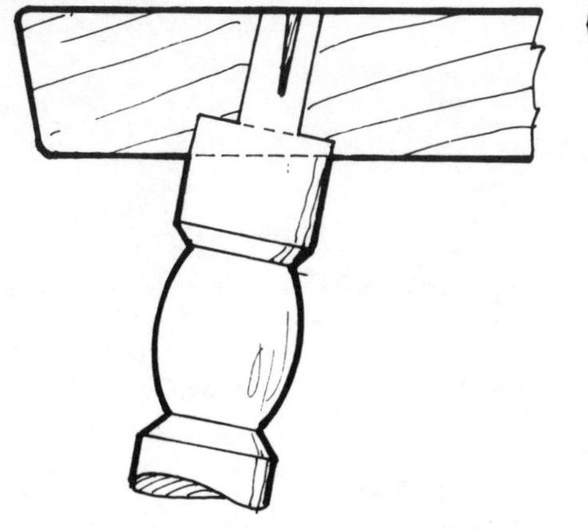

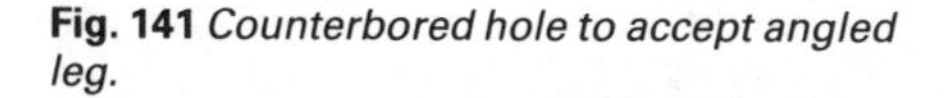

Fig. 141 *Counterbored hole to accept angled leg.*

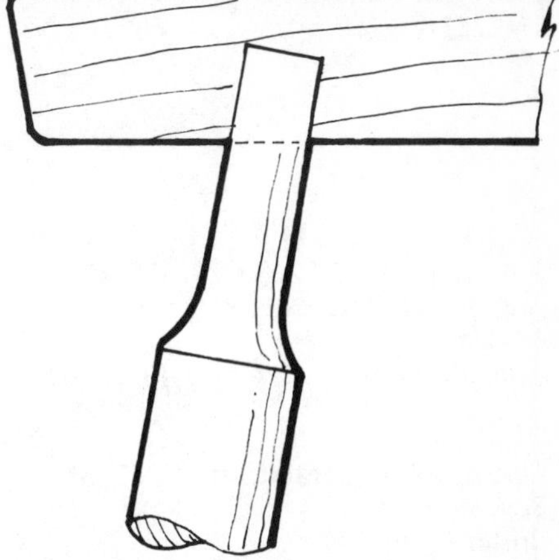

Fig. 142 *Turned component secured directly into blind hole.*

the member, bored to take the spigot. The hole should be bored first, then the spigot turned to suit the hole as it is easier to adjust the diameter of the spigot than the hole.

Where turned parts need to be set at a slight angle to the piece to which they are secured, not only must the hole be bored at the necessary angle, but it must be counterbored on the underside so that the top of the turned part is recessed in this. If this is not done, then the shoulder of the spigot will not abut properly. The alternative to this is to turn down the end of the component to correspond to the size of the hole into which it will be secured, but without any shoulder. If the hole is in a quite thick material, a blind hole can be made which therefore controls the relative position of the two parts. Accurate turning of the leg is required in order that the end of this can be driven fully home, and yet be a tight fit. On thin material, a through hole has to be bored and then wedging adopted to ensure a secure fixing. The exact extent of the penetration of the leg into the hole must be carefully controlled to ensure overall dimensions are correct.

Index